The
Birdwatcher's
Book of
Lists

The Birdwatcher's Book of Lists

LISTS FOR RECREATION AND RECORDKEEPING

DR. LESTER L. SHORT

Curator, Department of Ornithology
American Museum of Natural History

Illustrations by

JUAN LUIS G. VELA

LONGMEADOW
PRESS

A RUNNING HEADS BOOK

Published by Longmeadow Press, 201 High Ridge Road,
Stamford, Connecticut 06904.

THE BIRDWATCHER'S BOOK OF LISTS: Western Region
was conceived and produced by
Running Heads Incorporated
55 West 21 Street
New York, NY 10010

Editor: Rose K. Phillips
Art Director/Designer: Gael Towey
Original Paintings: Juan Luis G. Vela
Map Art: Michele Lerner

ISBN 0-681-41478-2

Typeset by David E. Seham Associates Inc., Typographers, Metuchen, N.J.
Color separations by Hong Kong Scanner Craft Company Ltd.
Printed and bound in Hong Kong by C & C Offset Printing Co., Ltd.
0 9 8 7 6 5 4 3 2 1

Companion volume: *The Birdwatcher's Book of Lists:
Eastern Region*, by Dr. Lester L. Short

The author thanks Jennifer F.M. Horne,
Mary Forsell, and Marta Hallett
for their helpful suggestions,
and Jennifer, especially, for her patience.

. . . .

This book is dedicated to all those working to
save birds and their habitats for posterity;
to the extent that we succeed,
those following will lead a richer life.

Contents

Introduction

PART 1

The Birding Lists

PART 2

The Maps

. . . .

APPENDIX SOURCES

This book of lists has been designed so that every birder can better organize and enjoy his or her birdwatching activities. The lists have been created to correspond to natural categories, in an effort to assist the birder in making correct identifications, and keeping a permanent record of these, and to educate the birder to other facets of ornithology. The lists in and of themselves, and the categories they represent, tell much about birds: their seasonality, plumage variations, and habitats. In fact, each list here has been organized so that it brings to the birder an understanding of natural groupings of birds, based variously on a common habitat; a particular group of birds that acts in a particular way; a single family, order, or genus of birds; the time of day, month, or year, when a group of birds engages in a particular activity; or the changing plumages of birds, based on the season of the year.

Rather than overwhelm the reader with illustrations that attempt to identify every species included here, we have chosen instead to portray only the more common, widespread, and conspicuous birds of the region covered; that is, the area of North America north of Mexico and west of the 100th meridian. We realize that any experienced birder would have his or her own selection of such species; this being the author's own. This book is *not* a field guide. In fact, it is an ancillary tool, one that should be used alongside any of the fine field guides available to the birder today.

The twenty-three lists offered here present common, regularly occurring species, and generally exclude unusual or uncommon birds. In dealing with less common species, the principle for the birder to follow is to consider a bird to represent the expected, common species *unless* it can be proved by its features that it is not such. The unexpected *can* happen; but birding, like any other science, generally works within the law of averages, so it should be presumed that the species sighted is the most common one.

This book has been written with the assumption that the birder will be viewing for the lists from one location. However, our range delineation—that is, north of Mexico west of the 100th meridian in North America—may change some species from "expected" to "unexpected." To help the birder cope with sightings with as much precision as possible, the symbols *N* for north, *S* for south, *E* for east, and *W* for west have been used. These symbols, in parentheses following the English name of the bird on the list, show restriction in occurrence of a species to the part of the region so specified.

The twenty-three lists have been compiled in an order that moves from the commoner, most conspicuous, species, to the most difficult, or those that would necessitate travel from a home environment for completion. This should help the birder to familiarize himself or herself with the techniques of birding, feel the accomplishment of compiling the lists, and move on, with ease, to the more ambitious, difficult lists.

Each of the lists here that have no designated time limitation—that is, in hours or season, for sightings—are presumed to be compiled in a single sighting period, for which the reader will set his or her own time frame. The larger lists relating to habitat are generally exclusive. In other words, a woodland species that enters overgrown pastures will be listed here as a "woodland" rather than a "field" bird. Some birds of open areas that enter open woodlands will be found on the "field" bird list. Those lists that deal with migrant species, as well as the *24-Hour Spring Field* list, involve selecting the most opportune time, or season, for the sighting. In the northwest, for example, mid-May and mid-September provide the seasons with the greatest range of available species. Farther south, the sightings must be accomplished earlier, in April, or, in the desert southwest, in March, to fall into the period considered as the "Spring" season for birds. In terms of time of day for compilation, the *24-Hour Spring Field* list should begin in the dark, in order to be able to spot the widest range of nightbirds. Some birders begin a twenty-four hour watch at 2:00 or 3:00 AM.

The list of *Female Waterfowl* includes fairly common species that have a distinctive female plumage. The *Immature Birds* species are also those with plumages that are distinct and carried by the birds for a long period: This may be a period of months in smaller birds; or years in some of the larger species. Note that most birds have two non-adult plumages, immature and juvenile, and some even have a downy young plumage. The downy plumage, however, is usually held for a short period, often only when the young are with their parents, so their identities can be discerned by their parents. Also omitted from the listing of immature birds are those young birds that essentially resemble the adult female so closely that they cannot be readily distinguished from her. It is interesting to note that most immature-plumaged birds show a greater resemblance to the adult female than the adult male, no matter which gender the offspring. The restricted lists, such as *Birds of Prey,* are based on frequently seen species that, in the cases of restriction, are only found in the specified area, or habitat.

Flight identification presents completely different problems for the birder than does the identification of perched species, so included here is a list for completion of those birds that are commonly seen in flight.

The *Vagrant Species* list has been designed as a personal tally, for which species are "vagrant" depends on the birder's location for sighting. Irregular events, such as hurricanes, which occur in diverse places, depending on their paths, can bring birds in from afar, but these events vary tremendously in terms of the birds that will be accidentally carried along and, fortunately, major hurricanes are not annual events.

Arctic birds, as defined here, are those species from the high Arctic that do not breed in southern Canada. These birds should be sought in winter, and are generally more likely to be observed in the north than in the south. Night birding should take place during the breeding season, in order to be able to sight the greatest number of species, in that these birds are more plentiful at this time of year. The breeding season for these birds generally means June in the mountains and the north, but may occur as early as April in the far south. Some species breed earlier than others, such as the Great Horned Owl, which commences nesting in the winter.

The *North American Travel* and *World Travel* lists have been designed to be constructed entirely by the reader. The source for the species in these lists should be the birder's field guide. Rather than catalogue some 9,000 species worldwide or the approximately 840 in North America alone, it is more expedient to allow the reader to compile a personal list.

In addition to the twenty-three lists, a section containing range maps has been included in the book, so that the reader can more precisely verify, by locale, whether a bird has been accurately sighted. Range information—incorporating habitat, resident, and winter patterns—can be one of the key factors in making a positive identification. Only rarely will a bird stray from its known habitat and flight pattern. The range maps here are meant to present a diverse array of the different patterns of distribution of birds, including residents, migrants that winter in a part of their breeding range, migrants that move over long distances, and wintering species.

In addition to the lists, illustrations, and range map information, also included is an "Appendix" that provides references, lists of Audubon Societies and addresses, and popular bird-watching periodicals.

English and scientific names used in the listings conform to the 1983 *American Ornithologists' Union Check-list of North American Birds,* Sixth Edition.

As mentioned previously, a good field guide is a necessity for every birdwatcher, and one must be used in conjunction with this book. Some excellent guides are available, including those that pertain to states, or even particular localities. A listing of these can be found in the bibliography in the *Appendix.*

In trying to identify a species, note, and jot down, if possible, all the visible characteristics *before* the bird disappears from sight. A micro-cassette recorder is a great help, for one can whisper characteristics without taking one's eyes from the bird. In addition to general color and size, try to determine the color of beak, legs, feet, and undertail feathers. Notice whether the bird has wing bars, an eye-ring, white on its tail; stripes on its body, a patch on its cheek, or a line over its eyes. Check the shape of its bill. Notice the size, habits, and habitats, and voice of the bird. Any one of these can be an important clue to the identity of the species. In many cases, the bird's English or scientific name is descriptive of one of these factors.

It is our hope that this book will assist you in enjoying North America's birds. Birdwatching is a lifelong "occupation," providing many thrills and enhancing the understanding of man's place in nature. Enjoy your birds and help as you can to preserve their habitats, for throughout the world, and especially in the tropics, we stand to lose for all time great numbers of species that those coming after us will never see and know. As our understanding of birds grows on a popular level, the greater will be our ability to preserve all the species for viewing by following generations.

LESTER L. SHORT

PART I

The Birding Lists

Birdfeeder Birds

PLACE

· · · · · · · · · · · · ·

SPECIES SIGHTED

· · · · · · · · · · · · ·

NUMBER

	♂	♀	JUV.	IMM.	
					DOVES
	—	—	—	—	Mourning Dove, *Zenaida macroura*
	—	—	—	—	Inca Dove, *Columbina inca*
	—	—	—	—	Common Ground-Dove, *Columbina passerina*
					HUMMINGBIRDS
	—	—	—	—	Ruby-throated Hummingbird, *Archilochus colubris*
	—	—	—	—	Black-chinned Hummingbird, *Archilochus alexandri*
	—	—	—	—	Anna's Hummingbird, *Calypte anna*
	—	—	—	—	Broad-tailed Hummingbird, *Selasphorus platycercus*
	—	—	—	—	Rufous Hummingbird, *Selasphorus rufus*
	—	—	—	—	Allen's Hummingbird, *Selasphorus sasin*
					WOODPECKERS
	—	—	—	—	Gila Woodpecker, *Melanerpes uropygialis*
	—	—	—	—	Downy Woodpecker, *Picoides pubescens*
	—	—	—	—	Hairy Woodpecker, *Picoides villosus*
	—	—	—	—	Northern Flicker, *Colaptes auratus*

♂ ♀ JUV. IMM.

JAYS, MAGPIES, AND CROWS

Gray Jay, *Perisoreus canadensis* ___ ___ ___ ___

Steller's Jay, *Cyanocitta stelleri* ___ ___ ___ ___

Scrub Jay, *Aphelocoma coerulescens* ___ ___ ___ ___

Pinyon Jay, *Gymnorhinus cyanocephalus* ___ ___ ___ ___

Clark's Nutcracker, *Nucifraga columbiana* ___ ___ ___ ___

American Crow, *Corvus brachyrhynchos* ___ ___ ___ ___

CHICKADEES AND TITMICE

Black-capped Chickadee, *Parus atricapillus* ___ ___ ___ ___

Mexican Chickadee, *Parus sclateri* ___ ___ ___ ___

Mountain Chickadee, *Parus gambeli* ___ ___ ___ ___

Chestnut-backed Chickadee, *Parus rufescens* ___ ___ ___ ___

Bridled Titmouse, *Parus wollweberi* ___ ___ ___ ___

Plain Titmouse, *Parus inornatus* ___ ___ ___ ___

♂	♀	JUV.	IMM.	NUTHATCHES, CREEPERS, AND THRUSHES
—	—	—	—	Red-breasted Nuthatch, *Sitta canadensis*
—	—	—	—	White-breasted Nuthatch, *Sitta carolinensis*
—	—	—	—	Brown Creeper, *Certhia americana*
—	—	—	—	Mountain Bluebird, *Sialia currucoides*
—	—	—	—	American Robin, *Turdus migratorius*

MOCKINGBIRDS, STARLINGS, AND WARBLERS

♂	♀	JUV.	IMM.	
—	—	—	—	Northern Mockingbird, *Mimus polyglottos*
—	—	—	—	European Starling, *Sturnus vulgaris*
—	—	—	—	Yellow-rumped Warbler, *Dendroica coronata*

TANAGERS AND ALLIES

♂	♀	JUV.	IMM.	
—	—	—	—	Western Tanager, *Piranga ludoviciana*
—	—	—	—	Northern Cardinal, *Cardinalis cardinalis*
—	—	—	—	Black-headed Grosbeak, *Pheucticus melanocephalus*

TOWHEES, SPARROWS, AND ALLIES

♂	♀	JUV.	IMM.	
—	—	—	—	Rufous-sided Towhee, *Pipilo erythrophthalmus*
—	—	—	—	Brown Towhee, *Pipilo fuscus*

	♂	♀	JUV.	IMM.
American Tree Sparrow, *Spizella arborea*	___	___	___	___
Chipping Sparrow, *Spizella passerina*	___	___	___	___
Black-throated Sparrow, *Amphispiza bilineata*	___	___	___	___
Fox Sparrow, *Passerella iliaca*	___	___	___	___
Song Sparrow, *Melospiza melodia*	___	___	___	___
Golden-crowned Sparrow, *Zonotrichia atricapilla*	___	___	___	___
White-crowned Sparrow, *Zonotrichia leucophrys*	___	___	___	___
Dark-eyed Junco, *Junco hyemalis*	___	___	___	___

FINCHES AND ALLIES

	♂	♀	JUV.	IMM.
Cassin's Finch, *Carpodacus cassinii*	___	___	___	___
House Finch, *Carpodacus mexicanus*	___	___	___	___
Common Redpoll, *Carduelis flammea*	___	___	___	___
Pine Siskin, *Carduelis pinus*	___	___	___	___
Lesser Goldfinch, *Carduelis psaltria*	___	___	___	___
Lawrence's Goldfinch (SW), *Carduelis lawrencei*	___	___	___	___
American Goldfinch, *Carduelis tristis*	___	___	___	___
Evening Grosbeak, *Coccothraustes verpertinus*	___	___	___	___
House Sparrow, *Passer domesticus*	___	___	___	___

COMMENTS AND SIGHTING NOTES

. . . .

Month-
by-
Month
Backyard
Birdwatch

FOR YEAR

....

A T

....

P L A C E

JANUARY		
FEBRUARY		
MARCH		
APRIL		
MAY		
JUNE		

J U L Y

_____ _____ _____

_____ _____ _____

A U G U S T

_____ _____ _____

_____ _____ _____

S E P T E M B E R

_____ _____ _____

_____ _____ _____

O C T O B E R

_____ _____ _____

_____ _____ _____

N O V E M B E R

_____ _____ _____

_____ _____ _____

D E C E M B E R

_____ _____ _____

_____ _____ _____

_____ _____ _____

**COMMENTS
AND
SIGHTING
NOTES**

. . . .

Nesting Yard Species

BEGINNING ON

. . . .

D A T E

**AND
ENDING ON**

. . . .

D A T E

AT

. . . .

P L A C E

SPECIES SIGHTED

(Fill in ♂, ♀, Juv., or Imm.)

DOVES

_____ Mourning Dove, *Zenaida macroura*

_____ Inca Dove, *Columbina inca*

_____ Common Ground-Dove, *Columbina passerina*

HUMMINGBIRDS

_____ Black-chinned Hummingbird, *Archilochus alexandri*

_____ Anna's Hummingbird, *Calypte anna*

_____ Rufous Hummingbird, *Selasphorus rufus*

_____ Allen's Hummingbird, *Selasphorus sasin*

WOODPECKERS

Acorn Woodpecker, *Melanerpes formicivorus* _____

Gila Woodpecker, *Melanerpes uropygialis* _____

Nuttall's Woodpecker, *Picoides nuttallii* _____

Downy Woodpecker, *Picoides pubescens* _____

Hairy Woodpecker, *Picoides villosus* _____

Northern Flicker, *Colaptes auratus* _____

SWALLOWS

Purple Martin, *Progne subis* _____

Cliff Swallow, *Hirundo pyrrhonota* _____

Barn Swallow, *Hirundo rustica* _____

JAYS AND CROWS

Steller's Jay, *Cyanocitta stelleri* _____

Scrub Jay, *Aphelocoma coerulescens* _____

American Crow, *Corvus brachyrhynchos* _____

CHICKADEES AND TITMICE

Black-capped Chickadee, *Parus atricapillus* _____

Mountain Chickadee, *Parus gambeli* _____

Chestnut-backed Chickadee, *Parus rufescens* _____

Plain Titmouse, *Parus inornatus* _____

NUTHATCHES AND WRENS

White-breasted Nuthatch, *Sitta carolinensis* _____

Cactus Wren, *Campylorhynchus brunneicapilus* _____

Bewick's Wren, *Thryomanes bewickii* _____

House Wren, *Troglodytes aedon* _____

COMMENTS AND SIGHTING NOTES

. . . .

SOLITAIRES AND THRUSHES

_____ Western Bluebird, *Sialia mexicana*

_____ Mountain Bluebird, *Sialia currucoides*

_____ American Robin, *Turdus migratorius*

MOCKINGBIRDS AND THRASHERS

_____ Northern Mockingbird, *Mimus polyglottos*

_____ Curve-billed Thrasher, *Toxostoma curvirostre*

_____ California Thrasher, *Toxostoma redivivum*

CARDINALS AND GROSBEAKS

_____ Northern Cardinal, *Cardinalis cardinalis*

_____ Black-headed Grosbeak, *Pheucticus melanocephalus*

TOWHEES, SPARROWS, AND ALLIES

_____ Rufous-sided Towhee, *Pipilo erythrophthalmus*

_____ Brown Towhee, *Pipilo fuscus*

_____ Chipping Sparrow, *Spizella passerina*

_____ White-crowned Sparrow, *Zonotrichia leucophrys*

_____ Dark-eyed Junco, *Junco hyemalis*

BLACKBIRDS AND ORIOLES

Brewer's Blackbird, *Euphagus cyanocephalus* ⎯⎯⎯

Brown-headed Cowbird, *Molothrus ater* ⎯⎯⎯

Hooded Oriole, *Icterus cucullatus* ⎯⎯⎯

Northern Oriole, *Icterus galbula* ⎯⎯⎯

FINCHES AND ALLIES

Purple Finch, *Carpodacus purpureus* ⎯⎯⎯

House Finch, *Carpodacus mexicanus* ⎯⎯⎯

House Sparrow, *Passer domesticus* ⎯⎯⎯

**COMMENTS
AND
SIGHTING
NOTES**

. . . .

Coastal Waterbirds

DATE	SPECIES SIGHTED

DATE

. . . .

PLACE

. . . .

SPECIES SIGHTED

. . . .

NUMBER

♂ ♀ JUV. IMM. **LOONS, GREBES, AND PELICANS**

—— —— —— —— Red-throated Loon, *Gavia stellata*

—— —— —— —— Common Loon, *Gavia immer*

—— —— —— —— Horned Grebe, *Podiceps auritus*

—— —— —— —— Eared Grebe, *Podiceps nigricollis*

—— —— —— —— Western Grebe (W), *Aechmophorus occidentalis*

—— —— —— —— American White Pelican, *Pelecanus erythrorhynchos*

—— —— —— —— Brown Pelican, *Pelecanus occidentalis*

CORMORANTS

—— —— —— —— Double-crested Cormorant, *Phalacrocorax auritus*

	♂	♀	JUV.	IMM.
Brandt's Cormorant, *Phalacrocorax penicillatus*	—	—	—	—
Pelagic Cormorant, *Phalacrocorax pelagicus*	—	—	—	—

H E R O N S

Great Blue Heron, *Ardea herodias*	—	—	—	—
Snowy Egret (S), *Egretta thula*	—	—	—	—
Black-crowned Night-Heron, *Nycticorax nycticorax*	—	—	—	—

D U C K S

Snow Goose, *Chen caerulescens*	—	—	—.	—
Canada Goose, *Branta canadensis*	—	—	—	—
Brant, *Branta bernicla*	—	—	—	—
Mallard, *Anas platyrhynchos*	—	—	—	—
Redhead, *Aythya americana*	—	—	—	—
Ring-necked Duck, *Aythya collaris*	—	—	—	—

♂	♀	JUV.	IMM.	
—	—	—	—	Greater Scaup, *Aythya marila*
—	—	—	—	Lesser Scaup, *Aythya affinis*
—	—	—	—	Harlequin Duck (N), *Histrionicus histrionicus*
—	—	—	—	Oldsquaw (N), *Clangula hyemalis*
—	—	—	—	Black Scoter (N), *Melanitta nigra*
—	—	—	—	Surf Scoter, *Melanitta perspicillata*
—	—	—	—	White-winged Scoter, *Melanitta fusca*
—	—	—	—	Common Goldeneye, *Bucephala clangula*
—	—	—	—	Barrow's Goldeneye (N), *Bucephala islandica*
—	—	—	—	Bufflehead, *Bucephala albeola*
—	—	—	—	Hooded Merganser, *Lophodytes cucullatus*
—	—	—	—	Common Merganser, *Mergus merganser*
—	—	—	—	Red-breasted Merganser, *Mergus serrator*
—	—	—	—	Ruddy Duck, *Oxyura jamaicensis*

EAGLES, HAWKS, RAILS, AND ALLIES

♂	♀	JUV.	IMM.	
—	—	—	—	Bald Eagle, *Haliaeetus leucocephalus*
—	—	—	—	Northern Harrier, *Circus cyaneus*
—	—	—	—	Clapper Rail (S), *Rallus longirostris*
—	—	—	—	Virginia Rail, *Rallus limicola*
—	—	—	—	Sora, *Porzana carolina*

	♂	♀	JUV.	IMM.
Common Moorhen, *Gallinula chloropus*	—	—	—	—
American Coot, *Fulica americana*	—	—	—	—

. . . .

PLOVERS AND OYSTERCATCHERS

	♂	♀	JUV.	IMM.
Black-bellied Plover, *Pluvialis squatarola*	—	—	—	—
Snowy Plover, *Charadrius alexandrinus*	—	—	—	—
Wilson's Plover, *Charadrius wilsonia*	—	—	—	—
Semipalmated Plover, *Charadrius semipalmatus*	—	—	—	—
American Black Oystercatcher, *Haematopus bachmani*	—	—	—	—

SANDPIPERS AND ALLIES

	♂	♀	JUV.	IMM.
Lesser Yellowlegs, *Tringa flavipes*	—	—	—	—
Solitary Sandpiper, *Tringa solitaria*	—	—	—	—
Willet, *Catoptrophorus semipalmatus*	—	—	—	—
Wandering Tattler, *Heteroscelus incanus*	—	—	—	—
Spotted Sandpiper, *Actitis macularia*	—	—	—	—
Whimbrel, *Numenius phaeopus*	—	—	—	—
Marbled Godwit, *Limosa fedoa*	—	—	—	—
Black Turnstone, *Arenaria melanocephala*	—	—	—	—
Surfbird, *Aphriza virgata*	—	—	—	—
Red Knot, *Calidris canutus*	—	—	—	—
Sanderling, *Calidris alba*	—	—	—	—

♂	♀	JUV.	IMM.	
—	—	—	—	Semipalmated Sandpiper, *Calidris pusilla*
—	—	—	—	Western Sandpiper, *Calidris mauri*
—	—	—	—	Least Sandpiper, *Calidris minutilla*
—	—	—	—	White-rumped Sandpiper, *Calidris fuscicollis*
—	—	—	—	Baird's Sandpiper, *Calidris bairdii*
—	—	—	—	Rock Sandpiper, *Calidris ptilocnemis*
—	—	—	—	Dunlin, *Calidris alpina*
—	—	—	—	Long-billed Dowitcher, *Limnodromus scolopaceus*

GULLS, TERNS, AND SKIMMERS

♂	♀	JUV.	IMM.	
—	—	—	—	Bonaparte's Gull, *Larus philadelphia*
—	—	—	—	Heermann's Gull (S), *Larus heermanni*
—	—	—	—	California Gull, *Larus californicus*
—	—	—	—	Herring Gull, *Larus argentatus*
—	—	—	—	Thayer's Gull, *Larus thayeri*
—	—	—	—	Western Gull, *Larus occidentalis*
—	—	—	—	Glaucous-winged Gull, *Larus glaucescens*
—	—	—	—	Caspian Tern, *Sterna caspia*
—	—	—	—	Elegant Tern (S), *Sterna elegans*
—	—	—	—	Common Tern, *Sterna hirundo*
—	—	—	—	Black Skimmer, *Rynchops niger*

MURRES AND PUFFINS	♂	♀	JUV.	IMM.
Common Murre, *Uria aalge*	—	—	—	—
Pigeon Guillemot, *Cepphus columba*	—	—	—	—
Marbled Murrelet, *Brachyramphus marmoratus*	—	—	—	—
Rhinoceros Auklet, *Cerorhinca monocerata*	—	—	—	—
Tufted Puffin, *Fratercula cirrhata*	—	—	—	—

OWLS, SWIFTS, AND ICINGFISHERS

	♂	♀	JUV.	IMM.
Short-eared Owl, *Asio flammeus*	—	—	—	—
Black Swift, *Cypseloides niger*	—	—	—	—
Belted Kingfisher, *Ceryle alcyon*	—	—	—	—

SWALLOWS, CROWS, AND PIPITS

	♂	♀	JUV.	IMM.
Violet-green Swallow, *Tachycineta thalassina*	—	—	—	—
Barn Swallow, *Hirundo rustica*	—	—	—	—
Northwestern Crow (N), *Corvus caurinus*	—	—	—	—
Water Pipit, *Anthus spinoletta*	—	—	—	—

SPARROWS AND BLACKBIRDS

	♂	♀	JUV.	IMM.
Savannah Sparrow, *Passerculus sandwichensis*	—	—	—	—
Song Sparrow, *Melospiza melodia*	—	—	—	—
Red-winged Blackbird (S), *Agelaius phoeniceus*	—	—	—	—

COMMENTS AND SIGHTING NOTES

. . . .

Inland Waterbirds

DATE

. . . .

PLACE

. . . .

**SPECIES
SIGHTED**

. . . .

NUMBER

SPECIES SIGHTED

♂ ♀ JUV. IMM. **GREBES AND
PELICANS**

—— —— —— —— Pied-billed Grebe, *Podilymbus
podiceps*

—— —— —— —— Eared Grebe, *Podiceps
nigricollis*

—— —— —— —— Western Grebe, *Aechmophorus
occidentalis*

—— —— —— —— American White Pelican,
Pelecanus erythrorhynchos

HERONS AND IBISES

	♂	♀	JUV.	IMM.
Great Blue Heron, *Ardea herodias*	___	___	___	___
Great Egret (S, W), *Casmerodius albus*	___	___	___	___
Snowy Egret (S), *Egretta thula*	___	___	___	___
Green-backed Heron, *Butorides striatus*	___	___	___	___
Black-crowned Night-Heron, *Nycticorax nycticorax*	___	___	___	___
Yellow-crowned Night-Heron, *Nycticorax violaecus*	___	___	___	___
White-faced Ibis, *Plegadis chihi*	___	___	___	___

♂	♀	JUV.	IMM.	**G E E S E A N D D U C K S**
—	—	—	—	Snow Goose, *Chen caerulescens*
—	—	—	—	Canada Goose, *Branta canadensis*
—	—	—	—	Wood Duck, *Aix sponsa*
—	—	—	—	Green-winged Teal, *Anas crecca*
—	—	—	—	Mallard, *Anas platyrhynchos*
—	—	—	—	Northern Pintail, *Anas acuta*
—	—	—	—	Blue-winged Teal, *Anas discors*
—	—	—	—	Cinnamon Teal, *Anas cyanoptera*
—	—	—	—	Northern Shoveler, *Anas clypeata*
—	—	—	—	Gadwall, *Anas strepera*
—	—	—	—	Canvasback, *Aythya valisineria*
—	—	—	—	Redhead, *Aythya americana*
—	—	—	—	Ring-necked Duck, *Aythya collaris*
—	—	—	—	Lesser Scaup, *Aythya affinis*
—	—	—	—	Common Goldeneye, *Bucephala clangula*
—	—	—	—	Bufflehead, *Bucephala albeola*
—	—	—	—	Common Merganser, *Mergus merganser*
—	—	—	—	Ruddy Duck, *Oxyura jamaicensis*

**E A G L E S ,   H A W K S ,
A N D   A L L I E S**

♂	♀	JUV.	IMM.	
—	—	—	—	Osprey, *Pandion haliaetus*
—	—	—	—	Bald Eagle, *Haliaeetus leucocephalus*
—	—	—	—	Northern Harrier, *Circus cyaneus*

RAILS, GALLINULES, COOTS, AND CRANES

	♂	♀	JUV.	IMM.

Yellow Rail, *Coturnicops noveboracensis* ___ ___ ___ ___

Virginia Rail, *Rallus limicola* ___ ___ ___ ___

Sora, *Porzana carolina* ___ ___ ___ ___

Common Moorhen, *Gallinula chloropus* ___ ___ ___ ___

American Coot, *Fulica americana* ___ ___ ___ ___

Sandhill Crane, *Grus canadensis* ___ ___ ___ ___

PLOVERS, STILTS, AVOCETS, SANDPIPERS, PHALAROPES, AND ALLIES

Killdeer, *Charadrius vociferus* ___ ___ ___ ___

Black-necked Stilt, *Himantopus mexicanus* ___ ___ ___ ___

American Avocet, *Recurvirostra americana* ___ ___ ___ ___

Willet, *Catoptrophorus semipalmatus* ___ ___ ___ ___

Long-billed Curlew, *Numenius americanus* ___ ___ ___ ___

Marbled Godwit, *Limosa fedoa* ___ ___ ___ ___

Sanderling, *Calidris alba* ___ ___ ___ ___

Semipalmated Sandpiper, *Calidris pusilla* ___ ___ ___ ___

Western Sandpiper, *Calidris mauri* ___ ___ ___ ___

Least Sandpiper, *Calidris minutilla* ___ ___ ___ ___

Pectoral Sandpiper, *Calidris melanotos* ___ ___ ___ ___

♂	♀	JUV.	IMM.	
___	___	___	___	Dunlin, *Calidris alpina*
___	___	___	___	Stilt Sandpiper, *Calidris himantopus*
___	___	___	___	Buff-breasted Sandpiper, *Tryngites subruficollis*
___	___	___	___	Common Snipe, *Gallinago gallinago*
___	___	___	___	Wilson's Phalarope, *Phalaropus tricolor*

GULLS AND TERNS

___	___	___	___	Franklin's Gull, *Larus pipixcan*
___	___	___	___	California Gull, *Larus californicus*
___	___	___	___	Caspian Tern, *Sterna caspia*
___	___	___	___	Common Tern, *Sterna hirundo*
___	___	___	___	Forster's Tern, *Sterna forsteri*
___	___	___	___	Black Tern, *Chlidonias niger*

KINGFISHERS

___	___	___	___	Belted Kingfisher, *Ceryle alcyon*

SWALLOWS

___	___	___	___	Tree Swallow, *Tachycineta bicolor*
___	___	___	___	Violet-green Swallow, *Tachycineta thalassina*
___	___	___	___	Bank Swallow, *Riparia riparia*
___	___	___	___	Barn Swallow, *Hirundo rustica*

CROWS

___	___	___	___	American Crow, *Corvus brachyrhynchos*

WRENS AND DIPPERS

	♂	♀	JUV.	IMM.
Sedge Wren, *Cistothorus platensis*	___	___	___	___
Marsh Wren, *Cistothorus palustris*	___	___	___	___
American Dipper, *Cinclus mexicanus*	___	___	___	___

PIPITS

Water Pipit, *Anthus spinoletta*	___	___	___	___

WARBLERS

Yellow Warbler, *Dendroica petechia*	___	___	___	___
Northern Waterthrush, *Seiurus noveboracensis*	___	___	___	___
Common Yellowthroat, *Geothlypis trichas*	___	___	___	___

SPARROWS

Savannah Sparrow, *Passerculus sandwichensis*	___	___	___	___
Song Sparrow, *Melospiza melodia*	___	___	___	___

BLACKBIRDS

Red-winged Blackbird, *Agelaius phoeniceus*	___	___	___	___
Yellow-headed Blackbird, *Xanthocephalus xanthocephalus*	___	___	___	___

FEMALE DUCKS AND ALLIES

Family Anatidae *(by Genus)*

STORKS, SWANS, GEESE, AND DUCKS

DATE

. . . .

PLACE

. . . .

SPECIES SIGHTED

. . . .

NUMBER

GENUS *Aix*
_____ Wood Duck, *Aix sponsa*

GENUS *Anas*
_____ Green-winged Teal, *Anas crecca*
_____ Mallard, *Anas platyrhynchos*
_____ Northern Pintail, *Anas acuta*
_____ Blue-winged Teal, *Anas discors*
_____ Cinnamon Teal, *Anas cyanoptera*
_____ Northern Shoveler, *Anas clypeata*
_____ Gadwall, *Anas strepera*
_____ American Wigeon, *Anas americana*

GENUS *Aythya*
Canvasback, *Aythya valisineria* _____
Redhead, *Aythya americana* _____
Greater Scaup, *Aythya marila* _____
Lesser Scaup, *Aythya affinis* _____

GENUS *Histrionicus*
Harlequin Duck, *Histrionicus histrionicus* _____

GENUS *Melanitta*
White-winged Scoter, *Melanitta fusca* _____

GENUS *Bucephala*
Common Goldeneye, *Bucephala clangula* _____
Barrow's Goldeneye, *Bucephala islandica* _____

GENUS *Lophodytes*
Hooded Merganser, *Lophodytes cucullatus* _____

GENUS *Mergus*
Common Merganser, *Mergus merganser* _____

GENUS *Oxyura*
Ruddy Duck, *Oxyura jamaicensis* _____

SPECIES SIGHTED

♂ ♀ **PELICANS AND HERONS**

___ ___ Brown Pelican, *Pelecanus occidentalis*

___ ___ Black-crowned Night-Heron, *Nycticorax nycticorax*

DATE

. . . .

PLACE

. . . .

SPECIES SIGHTED

. . . .

NUMBER

EAGLES, HAWKS, AND FALCONS

___ ___ Bald Eagle, *Haliaeetus luecocephalus*

___ ___ Cooper's Hawk, *Accipiter cooperii*

___ ___ Red-tailed Hawk, *Buteo jamaicensis*

___ ___ Ferruginous Hawk, *Buteo regalis*

___ ___ Rough-legged Hawk, *Buteo lagopus*

___ ___ Golden Eagle, *Aquila chrysaetos*

___ ___ Merlin, *Falco columbarius*

___ ___ Peregrine Falcon, *Falco peregrinus*

GALLINULES

___ ___ Common Moorhen, *Gallinula chloropus*

GULLS

___ ___ Franklin's Gull, *Larus pipixcan*

___ ___ Bonaparte's Gull, *Larus philadelphia*

___ ___ Heermann's Gull, *Larus heermanni*

___ ___ Ring-billed Gull, *Larus delawarensis*

___ ___ California Gull, *Larus californicus*

___ ___ Herring Gull, *Larus argentatus*

___ ___ Western Gull, *Larus occidentalis*

___ ___ Glaucous-winged Gull, *Larus glaucescens*

OWLS AND SAPSUCKERS ♂ ♀

Northern Saw-whet Owl, *Aegolius acadicus* ___ ___

Red-naped Sapsucker, *Sphyrapicus nuchalis* ___ ___

Williamson's Sapsucker, *Sphyrapicus thyroideus* ___ ___

SWALLOWS AND THRUSHES

Tree Swallow, *Tachycineta bicolor* ___ ___

American Robin, *Turdus migratorius* ___ ___

STARLINGS, WARBLERS, GROSBEAKS AND SPARROWS

European Starling, *Sturnus vulgaris* ___ ___

Yellow-rumped Warbler, *Dendroica coronata* ___ ___

American Redstart, *Setophaga ruticilla* ___ ___

Blue Grosbeak, *Guiraca caerulea* ___ ___

Chipping Sparrow, *Spizella passerina* ___ ___

Black-chinned Sparrow, *Spizella atrogularis* ___ ___

BLACKBIRDS AND ORIOLES

Red-winged Blackbird, *Agelaius phoeniceus* ___ ___

Hooded Oriole, *Icterus cucullatus* ___ ___

Northern Oriole, *Icterus galbula* ___ ___

COMMENTS AND SIGHTING NOTES

. . . .

SIGHTINGS OF VULTURES, EAGLES, AND HAWKS

Families Cathartidae, Accipitridae, *and* Falconidae

♂　♀　JUV.　IMM.　V U L T U R E S

—— —— —— —— Black Vulture (S), *Coragyps atratus*

—— —— —— —— Turkey Vulture, *Cathartes aura*

—— —— —— —— California Condor, *Gymnogyps californianus*

D A T E

. . . .

P L A C E

. . . .

**S P E C I E S
S I G H T E D**

. . . .

N U M B E R

K I T E S ,   E A G L E S ,
H A W K S ,   A N D
A L L I E S

—— —— —— —— Osprey, *Pandion haliaetus*

—— —— —— —— Black-shouldered Kite (S), *Elanus caeruleus*

—— —— —— —— Bald Eagle, *Haliaeetus leucocephalus*

—— —— —— —— Northern Harrier, *Circus cyaneus*

—— —— —— —— Sharp-shinned Hawk, *Accipiter striatus*

—— —— —— —— Common Black-Hawk, *Buteogallus anthracinus*

—— —— —— —— Harris' Hawk, *Parabuteo unicinctus*

—— —— —— —— Gray Hawk, *Buteo nitidus*

—— —— —— —— Swainson's Hawk, *Buteo swainsoni*

—— —— —— —— Zone-tailed Hawk, *Buteo albonotatus*

—— —— —— —— Red-tailed Hawk, *Buteo jamaicensis*

	♂	♀	JUV.	IMM.
Ferruginous Hawk, *Buteo regalis*	—	—	—	—
Rough-legged Hawk, *Buteo lagopus*	—	—	—	—
Golden Eagle, *Aquila chrysaetos*	—	—	—	—

FALCONS

	♂	♀	JUV.	IMM.
American Kestrel, *Falco sparverius*	—	—	—	—
Merlin, *Falco columbarius*	—	—	—	—
Peregrine Falcon, *Falco peregrinus*	—	—	—	—
Gyrfalcon, *Falco rusticolus*	—	—	—	—
Prairie Falcon, *Falco mexicanus*	—	—	—	—

COMMENTS AND SIGHTING NOTES

. . . .

Woodland Birds in Spring Plumages

SPECIES SIGHTED

(Fill in ♂, ♀, Juv., or Imm.)

HERONS

_____ Reddish Egret, *Egretta rufescens*

_____ Green-backed Heron (W), *Butorides striatus*

DUCKS

_____ Wood Duck (W), *Aix sponsa*

_____ Common Goldeneye (N), *Bucephala clangula*

_____ Barrow's Goldeneye (N), *Bucephala islandica*

_____ Bufflehead, *Bucephala albeola*

_____ Hooded Merganser (N), *Lophodytes cucullatus*

VULTURES

_____ Turkey Vulture, *Cathartes aura*

HAWKS

_____ Sharp-shinned Hawk, *Accipiter striatus*

_____ Cooper's Hawk, *Accipiter cooperii*

_____ Northern Goshawk, *Accipiter gentilis*

_____ Common Black-Hawk (S), *Buteogallus anthracinus*

_____ Red-shouldered Hawk (SW), *Buteo lineatus*

_____ Zone-tailed Hawk (S), *Buteo albonotatus*

_____ Red-tailed Hawk, *Buteo jamaicensis*

_____ Golden Eagle, *Aquila chrysaetos*

FALCONS

_____ Merlin (N), *Falco columbarius*

GROUSE, TURKEYS, AND QUAIL

_____ Spruce Grouse (N), *Dendragapus canadensis*

_____ Blue Grouse, *Dendragapus obscurus*

Ruffed Grouse (N), *Bonasa umbellus* _____

Wild Turkey, *Meleagris gallopavo* _____

Scaled Quail (SE), *Callipepla squamata* _____

California Quail (W), _____
Callipepla californica

Mountain Quail (W), _____
Oreortyx pictus

PIGEONS AND CUCKOOS

Band-tailed Pigeon, _____
Columba fasciata
Yellow-billed Cuckoo, _____
Coccyzus americanus

OWLS AND GOATSUCKERS

Flammulated Owl, _____
Otus flammeolus
Western Screech-Owl, _____
Otus kennicottii

Great Horned Owl, _____
Bubo virginianus
Northern Pygmy-Owl, _____
Glaucidium gnoma

Spotted Owl, *Strix occidentalis* _____

Great Gray Owl (N), *Strix nebulosa* _____

Long-eared Owl, *Asio otus* _____

Boreal Owl (E), *Aegolius funereus* _____

Northern Saw-whet Owl (N), _____
Aegolius acadicus
Whip-poor-will (S), _____
Caprimulgus vociferus

SWIFTS AND HUMMINGBIRDS

Chimney Swift, *Chaetura pelagica* _____

Vaux's Swift (W), *Chaetura vauxi* _____

_____ Blue-throated Hummingbird (S), *Lampornis clemenciae*

_____ Magnificent Hummingbird (S), *Eugenes fulgens*

_____ Anna's Hummingbird (W), *Calypte anna*

_____ Costa's Hummingbird (S), *Calypte costae*

_____ Calliope Hummingbird, *Stellula calliope*

_____ Broad-tailed Hummingbird, *Selasphorus platycercus*

_____ Rufous Hummingbird (N), *Selasphorus rufus*

_____ Allen's Hummingbird, *Selasphorus sasin*

WOODPECKERS

_____ Lewis' Woodpecker, *Melanerpes lewis*

_____ Acorn Woodpecker (W), *Melanerpes formicivorus*

_____ Gila Woodpecker (S), *Melanerpes uropygialis*

_____ Red-naped Sapsucker, *Sphyrapicus nuchalis*

_____ Red-breasted Sapsucker (NW), *Sphyrapicus ruber*

_____ Williamson's Sapsucker, *Sphyrapicus thyroideus*

_____ Ladder-backed Woodpecker (S), *Picoides scalaris*

_____ Nuttall's Woodpecker (W), *Picoides nuttallii*

_____ Downy Woodpecker, *Picoides pubescens*

_____ Hairy Woodpecker, *Picoides villosus*

_____ White-headed Woodpecker (W), *Picoides albolarvatus*

_____ Three-toed Woodpecker (N), *Picoides tridactylus*

_____ Black-backed Woodpecker (N), *Picoides arcticus*

_____ Northern Flicker, *Colaptes auratus*

_____ Pileated Woodpecker (N), *Dryocopus pileatus*

FLYCATCHERS AND SWALLOWS

Olive-sided Flycatcher, *Mionectes olivaceus* _____

Western Wood-Pewee, *Contopus sordidulus* _____

Hammond's Flycatcher (N), *Empidonax hammondii* _____

Dusky Flycatcher, *Empidonax oberholseri* _____

Gray Flycatcher, *Empidonax wrightii* _____

Western Flycatcher, *Empidonax difficilis* _____

Black Phoebe (S), *Sayornis nigricans* _____

Vermilion Flycatcher (S), *Pyrocephalus rubinus* _____

Ash-throated Flycatcher, *Myiarchus cinerascens* _____

Cassin's Kingbird, *Tyrannus vociferans* _____

Eastern Kingbird (N), *Tyrannus tyrannus* _____

Tree Swallow (N), *Tachycineta bicolor* _____

Violet-green Swallow, *Tachycineta thalassina* _____

JAYS, MAGPIES, AND CROWS

Gray Jay (N), *Perisoreus canadensis* _____

Steller's Jay, *Cyanocitta stelleri* _____

Scrub Jay (S), *Aphelocoma coerulescens* _____

Pinyon Jay, *Gymnorhinus cyanocephalus* _____

Clark's Nutcracker, *Nucifraga columbiana* _____

Black-billed Magpie, *Pica pica* _____

American Crow, *Corvus brachyrhynchos* _____

Northwestern Crow (NW), *Corvus caurinus* _____

Common Raven, *Corvus corax* _____

CHICKADEES, TITMICE, AND ALLIES

Black-capped Chickadee (N), *Parus atricapillus* _____

_____ Mountain Chickadee, *Parus gambeli*

_____ Boreal Chickadee (N), *Parus budsonicus*

_____ Chestnut-backed Chickadee (N), *Parus rufescens*

_____ Plain Titmouse, *Parus inornatus*

_____ Bushtit, *Psaltriparus minimus*

NUTHATCHES, CREEPERS, WRENS, AND DIPPERS

_____ Red-breasted Nuthatch, *Sitta canadensis*

_____ White-breasted Nuthatch, *Sitta carolinensis*

_____ Pgymy Nuthatch, *Sitta pygmaea*

_____ Brown Creeper, *Certhia americana*

_____ Bewick's Wren (S), *Thryomanes bewickii*

_____ House Wren, *Troglodytes aedon*

_____ Winter Wren (N), *Troglodytes troglodytes*

_____ American Dipper, *Cinclus mexicanus*

KINGLETS, SOLITAIRES, THRUSHES, AND ALLIES

_____ Golden-crowned Kinglet, *Regulus satrapa*

_____ Ruby-crowned Kinglet, *Regulus calendula*

_____ Western Bluebird, *Sialia mexicana*

_____ Mountain Bluebird, *Sialia currucoides*

_____ Townsend's Solitaire, *Myadestes townsendi*

_____ Veery (N), *Catharus fuscescens*

_____ Swainson's Thrush (N), *Catharus ustulatus*

_____ American Robin, *Turdus migratorius*

_____ Varied Thrush (NW), *Ixoreus naevius*

_____ Wrentit (W), *Chamaea fasciata*

MOCKINGBIRDS AND THRASHERS

Gray Catbird (N), *Dumetella carolinensis* _____

Northern Mockingbird (S), *Mimus polyglottos* _____

California Thrasher (W), *Toxostoma redivivum* _____

WAXWINGS, PHAINOPEPLA, STARLINGS, AND VIREOS

Cedar Waxwing (N), *Bombycilla cedrorum* _____

Phainopepla (S), *Phainopepla nitens* _____

European Starling, *Sturnus vulgaris* _____

Bell's Vireo (S), *Vireo bellii* _____

Gray Vireo (S), *Vireo vicinior* _____

Solitary Vireo, *Vireo solitarius* _____

Hutton's Vireo (W), *Vireo huttoni* _____

Warbling Vireo, *Vireo gilvus* _____

Red-eyed Vireo (N), *Vireo olivaceus* _____

WARBLERS

Orange-crowned Warbler, *Vermivora celata* _____

Nashville Warbler (N), *Vermivora ruficapilla* _____

Virginia's Warbler (S), *Vermivora virginiae* _____

Yellow Warbler, *Dendroica petechia* _____

Yellow-rumped Warbler (N), *Dendroica coronata* _____

Black-throated Gray Warbler, *Dendroica nigrescens* _____

Townsend's Warbler (NW), *Dendroica townsendi* _____

Hermit Warbler (W), *Dendroica occidentalis* _____

Grace's Warbler (S), *Dendroica graciae* _____

American Redstart, *Setophaga ruticilla* _____

Northern Waterthrush (N), *Seiurus noveboracensis* _____

_____ MacGillivray's Warbler, *Oporornis tolmiei*

_____ Common Yellowthroat, *Geothlypis trichas*

_____ Wilson's Warbler, *Wilsonia pusilla*

_____ Red-faced Warbler (S), *Cardellina rubrifrons*

_____ Painted Redstart (S), *Myioborus pictus*

TANAGERS AND GROSBEAKS

_____ Hepatic Tanager (S), *Piranga flava*

_____ Summer Tanager (S), *Piranga rubra*

_____ Western Tanager, *Piranga ludoviciana*

_____ Black-headed Grosbeak, *Pheucticus melanocephalus*

_____ Blue Grosbeak (S), *Guiraca caerulea*

_____ Varied Bunting (S), *Passerina versicolor*

TOWHEES, SPARROWS, AND ALLIES

_____ Green-tailed Towhee, *Pipilo chlorurus*

_____ Rufous-sided Towhee, *Pipilo erythrophthalmus*

_____ Brown Towhee (S), *Pipilo fuscus*

_____ Abert's Towhee (SW), *Pipilo aberti*

_____ Chipping Sparrow, *Spizella passerina*

_____ Black-chinned Sparrow (SW), *Spizella atrogularis*

_____ Lark Sparrow, *Chondestes grammacus*

Henslow's Sparrow, *Ammodramus henslowii* _____

Fox Sparrow, *Passerella iliaca* _____

Song Sparrow, *Melospiza melodia* _____

Lincoln's Sparrow (N), *Melospiza lincolnii* _____

Swamp Sparrow (NE), *Melospiza georgiana* _____

Golden-crowned Sparrow (N), *Zonotrichia* _____
atricapilla

White-crowned Sparrow, *Zonotrichia* _____
leucophrys

Dark-eyed Junco (N), *Junco hyemalis* _____

Yellow-eyed Junco (S), *Junco phaeonotus* _____

BLACKBIRDS, ORIOLES,
FINCHES, AND ALLIES

Common Grackle (NE), *Quiscalus quiscula* _____

Brown-headed Cowbird, *Molothrus ater* _____

Hooded Oriole (S), *Icterus cucullatus* _____

Northern Oriole, *Icterus galbula* _____

Pine Grosbeak, *Pinicola enucleator* _____

Purple Finch (W), *Carpodacus purpureus* _____

Cassin's Finch, *Carpodacus cassinii* _____

House Finch, *Carpodacus mexicanus* _____

Red Crossbill, *Loxia curvirostra* _____

White-winged Crossbill (N), *Loxia leucoptera* _____

Pine Siskin, *Carduelis pinus* _____

Evening Grosbeak, *Coccothraustes* _____
verpertinus

The Nightbird Search

BEGINNING AT

. . . .
T   I   M   E

**AND
ENDING AT**

. . . .
T   I   M   E

ON

. . . .
D   A   T   E

AT

. . . .
P   L   A   C   E

SPECIES SIGHTED

(Fill in ♂, ♀, Juv., or Imm.)

_____ Common Barn-Owl, *Tyto alba*

_____ Flammulated Owl, *Otus flammeolus*

_____ Western Screech-Owl, *Otus kennicottii*

_____ Great Horned Owl, *Bubo virginianus*

_____ Northern Pygmy-Owl, *Glaucidium gnoma*

_____ Elf Owl, *Micrathene whitneyi*

_____ Burrowing Owl, *Athene cunicularia*

_____ Spotted Owl, *Strix occidentalis*

_____ Barred Owl, *Strix varia*

_____ Boreal Owl, *Aegolius funereus*

_____ Northern Saw-whet Owl, *Aegolius acadicus*

_____ Lesser Nighthawk, *Chordeiles acutipennis*

_____ Common Nighthawk, *Chordeiles minor*

_____ Common Poorwill, *Phalaenoptilus nuttallii*

_____ Whip-poor-will, *Caprimulgus vociferus*

The
24-Hour
Spring
Field
Birdwatch

DATE

. . . .

PLACE

. . . .

**SPECIES
SIGHTED**

. . . .

N U M B E R

SPECIES SIGHTED

♂ ♀ JUV. IMM. BITTERNS,
HERONS, AND
IBISES

— — — — American Bittern, *Botaurus lentiginosus*

— — — — Least Bittern (W), *Ixobrychus exilis*

— — — — Cattle Egret (S), *Bubulcus ibis*

— — — — White-faced Ibis, *Plegadis chihi*

GEESE AND
DUCKS

— — — — Canada Goose (N), *Branta canadensis*

— — — — Green-winged Teal, *Anas crecca*

— — — — Mallard, *Anas platyrhynchos*

— — — — Northern Pintail, *Anas acuta*

— — — — Blue-winged Teal (N), *Anas discors*

— — — — Cinnamon Teal, *Anas cyanoptera*

— — — — Northern Shoveler, *Anas clypeata*

	♂	♀	JUV.	IMM.
Canvasback (N), *Aythya valisineria*	___	___	___	___
Redhead, *Aythya americana*	___	___	___	___

V U L T U R E S

Turkey Vulture, *Cathartes aura*	___	___	___	___

E A G L E S , H A W K S , A N D   F A L C O N S

Northern Harrier, *Circus cyaneus*	___	___	___	___
Swainson's Hawk, *Buteo swainsoni*	___	___	___	___
Red-tailed Hawk, *Buteo jamaicensis*	___	___	___	___
Ferruginous Hawk, *Buteo regalis*	___	___	___	___
Golden Eagle, *Aquila chrysaetos*	___	___	___	___
American Kestrel, *Falco sparverius*	___	___	___	___
Peregrine Falcon, *Falco peregrinus*	___	___	___	___
Prairie Falcon, *Falco mexicanus*	___	___	___	___

♂	♀	JUV.	IMM.	PARTRIDGES, GROUSE, AND QUAIL
—	—	—	—	Gray Partridge (N), *Perdix perdix*
—	—	—	—	Chukar, *Alectoris chukar*
—	—	—	—	Ring-necked Pheasant (N), *Phasianus colchicus*
—	—	—	—	Sage Grouse, *Centrocercus urophasianus*
—	—	—	—	Lesser Prairie-Chicken (SE), *Tympanuchus pallidicinctus*
—	—	—	—	Sharp-tailed Grouse (NE), *Tympanuchus phasianellus*
—	—	—	—	Montezuma Quail (S), *Cyrtonyx montezumae*
—	—	—	—	Gambel's Quail (S), *Callipepla gambelii*

RAILS, GALLINULES, AND CRANES

—	—	—	—	Yellow Rail, *Coturnicops noveboracensis*
—	—	—	—	Sora (N), *Porzana carolina*
—	—	—	—	Common Moorhen (S), *Gallinula chloropus*
—	—	—	—	Sandhill Crane, *Grus canadensis*

PLOVERS, SANDPIPERS, AND ALLIES

—	—	—	—	Killdeer, *Charadrius vociferus*
—	—	—	—	Mountain Plover, *Charadrius montanus*
—	—	—	—	Willet (N), *Catoptrophorus semipalmatus*
—	—	—	—	Upland Sandpiper (N), *Bartramia longicauda*

	♂	♀	JUV.	IMM.

Long-billed Curlew (N), *Numenius americanus*   ___ ___ ___ ___

Marbled Godwit (NE), *Limosa fedoa*   ___ ___ ___ ___

P I G E O N S ,   D O V E S , A N D   A L L I E S

Rock Dove, *Columba livia*   ___ ___ ___ ___

Mourning Dove, *Zenaida macroura*   ___ ___ ___ ___

Greater Roadrunner (S), *Geococcyx californianus*   ___ ___ ___ ___

O W L S   A N D G O A T S U C K E R S

Burrowing Owl, *Athene cunicularia*   ___ ___ ___ ___

Short-eared Owl (N), *Asio flammeus*   ___ ___ ___ ___

Lesser Nighthawk (S), *Chordeiles acutipennis*   ___ ___ ___ ___

Common Nighthawk, *Chordeiles minor*   ___ ___ ___ ___

Common Poorwill, *Phalaenoptilus nuttallii*   ___ ___ ___ ___

S W I F T S   A N D H U M M I N G B I R D S

Chimney Swift, *Chaetura pelagica*   ___ ___ ___ ___

Vaux's Swift (W), *Chaetura vauxi*   ___ ___ ___ ___

Black-chinned Hummingbird, *Archilochus alexandri*   ___ ___ ___ ___

W O O D P E C K E R S

Lewis' Woodpecker, *Melanerpes lewis*   ___ ___ ___ ___

♂	♀	JUV.	IMM.	
——	——	——	——	Northern Flicker, *Colaptes auratus*

FLYCATCHERS, LARKS, AND SWALLOWS

♂	♀	JUV.	IMM.	
——	——	——	——	Willow Flycatcher, *Empidonax traillii*
——	——	——	——	Say's Phoebe, *Sayornis saya*
——	——	——	——	Horned Lark, *Eremophila alpestris*
——	——	——	——	Purple Martin, *Progne subis*
——	——	——	——	Tree Swallow (N), *Tachycineta bicolor*
——	——	——	——	Violet-green Swallow, *Tachycineta thalassina*
——	——	——	——	Northern Rough-winged Swallow, *Stelgidopteryx serripennis*
——	——	——	——	Bank Swallow, *Riparia riparia*
——	——	——	——	Cliff Swallow, *Hirundo pyrrhonota*
——	——	——	——	Barn Swallow, *Hirundo rustica*

CROWS

♂	♀	JUV.	IMM.	
——	——	——	——	American Crow, *Corvus brachyrhynchos*

WRENS

♂	♀	JUV.	IMM.	
——	——	——	——	Rock Wren, *Salpinctes obsoletus*
——	——	——	——	Canyon Wren, *Catherpes mexicanus*
——	——	——	——	Carolina Wren, *Thryothorus ludovicianus*
——	——	——	——	Bewick's Wren (S), *Thryomanes bewickii*

	♂	♀	JUV.	IMM.
Sedge Wren (NE), *Cistothorus platensis*	——	——	——	——

THRUSHES

American Robin, *Turdus migratorius*	——	——	——	——

MOCKINGBIRDS, THRASHERS, AND PIPITS

Northern Mockingbird (S), *Mimus polyglottos*	——	——	——	——
Sage Thrasher, *Oreoscoptes montanus*	——	——	——	——
Curve-billed Thrasher (S), *Toxostoma curvirostre*	——	——	——	——
Crissal Thrasher, *Toxostoma dorsale*	——	——	——	——
Water Pipit, *Anthus spinoletta*	——	——	——	——
Sprague's Pipit (NE), *Anthus spragueii*	——	——	——	——

SHRIKES AND STARLINGS

Loggerhead Shrike, *Lanius ludovicianus*	——	——	——	——
European Starling, *Sturnus vulgaris*	——	——	——	——

WARBLERS

Lucy's Warbler (S), *Vermivora luciae*	——	——	——	——
MacGillivray's Warbler, *Oporornis tolmiei*	——	——	——	——
Common Yellowthroat, *Geothlypis trichas*	——	——	——	——
Yellow-breasted Chat, *Icteria virens*	——	——	——	——

♂   ♀   JUV.   IMM.

GROSBEAKS

— — — — Lazuli Bunting, *Passerina amoena*

— — — — Dickcissel (E), *Spiza americana*

SPARROWS AND ALLIES

— — — — Cassin's Sparrow (SE), *Aimophila cassinii*

— — — — Rufous-crowned Sparrow (S), *Aimophila ruficeps*

— — — — Chipping Sparrow, *Spizella passerina*

— — — — Clay-colored Sparrow (NE), *Spizella pallida*

— — — — Brewer's Sparrow, *Spizella breweri*

— — — — Black-chinned Sparrow (SW), *Spizella atrogularis*

— — — — Vesper Sparrow, *Pooecetes gramineus*

— — — — Black-throated Sparrow (S), *Amphispiza bilineata*

— — — — Sage Sparrow, *Amphispiza belli*

— — — — Lark Bunting (NE), *Calamospiza melanocorys*

— — — — Savannah Sparrow (N), *Passerculus sandwichensis*

— — — — Henslow's Sparrow (N), *Ammodramus henslowii*

— — — — Sharp-tailed Sparrow (N), *Ammodramus caudacutus*

— — — — McCown's Longspur (NE), *Calcarius mccownii*

— — — — Chestnut-collared Longspur (NE), *Calcarius ornatus*

	♂	♀	JUV.	IMM.

MEADOWLARKS AND BLACKBIRDS

Bobolink (N), *Dolichonyx oryzivorus* ____ ____ ____ ____

Red-winged Blackbird, *Agelaius phoeniceus* ____ ____ ____ ____

Tricolored Blackbird (W), *Agelaius tricolor* ____ ____ ____ ____

Western Meadowlark, *Sturnella neglecta* ____ ____ ____ ____

Yellow-headed Blackbird, *Xanthocephalus xanthocephalus* ____ ____ ____ ____

Brewer's Blackbird, *Euphagus cyanocephalus* ____ ____ ____ ____

Great-tailed Grackle, *Quiscalus mexicanus* ____ ____ ____ ____

Common Grackle (NE), *Quiscalus quiscula* ____ ____ ____ ____

Bronzed Cowbird (S), *Molothrus aeneus* ____ ____ ____ ____

Brown-headed Cowbird, *Molothrus ater* ____ ____ ____ ____

FINCHES AND ALLIES

Rosy Finch (NE), *Leucosticte arctoa* ____ ____ ____ ____

House Finch, *Carpodacus mexicanus* ____ ____ ____ ____

Lesser Goldfinch (S), *Carduelis psaltria* ____ ____ ____ ____

Lawrence's Goldfinch (SW), *Carduelis lawrencei* ____ ____ ____ ____

American Goldfinch (N), *Carduelis tristis* ____ ____ ____ ____

SIGHTINGS OF WOOD WARBLERS:

Subfamily Parulinae

♂	♀	JUV.	IMM.	GENUS *Vermivora*
—	—	—	—	Orange-crowned Warbler, *Vermivora celata*
—	—	—	—	Nashville Warbler, *Vermivora ruficapilla*
—	—	—	—	Virginia's Warbler (S), *Vermivora virginiae*
—	—	—	—	Lucy's Warbler (S), *Vermivora luciae*
				GENUS *Dendroica*
—	—	—	—	Yellow Warbler, *Dendroica petechia*
—	—	—	—	Yellow-rumped Warbler, *Dendroica coronata*
—	—	—	—	Black-throated Gray Warbler, *Dendroica nigrescens*
—	—	—	—	Townsend's Warbler (W), *Dendroica townsendi*
—	—	—	—	Hermit Warbler (W), *Dendroica occidentalis*
—	—	—	—	Grace's Warbler (S), *Dendroica graciae*
—			—	Blackpoll Warbler (E), *Dendroica striata*

DATE

. . . .

PLACE

. . . .

SPECIES SIGHTED

. . . .

N U M B E R

GENUS *Mniotilta*	♂	♀	JUV.	IMM.
Black-and-white Warbler (E), *Mniotilta varia*	——	——	——	——

GENUS *Setophaga*

American Redstart, *Setophaga ruticilla* —— —— —— ——

GENUS *Seiurus*

Ovenbird, *Seiurus aurocapillus* —— —— —— ——

Northern Waterthrush, *Seiurus noveboracensis* —— —— —— ——

GENUS *Oporornis*

MacGillivray's Warbler, *Oporornis tolmiei* —— —— —— ——

GENUS *Geothlypis*

Common Yellowthroat, *Geothlypis trichas* —— —— —— ——

GENUS *Wilsonia*

Wilson's Warbler, *Wilsonia pusilla* —— —— —— ——

GENUS *Cardellina*

Red-faced Warbler (SW), *Cardellina rubrifrons* —— —— —— ——

GENUS *Myioborus*

Painted Redstart (SW), *Myioborus pictus* —— —— —— ——

GENUS *Icteria*

Yellow-breasted Chat, *Icteria virens* —— —— —— ——

GENUS *Peucedramus*

Olive Warbler (SW), *Peucedramus taeniatus* —— —— —— ——

Year List of Birds in Flight

♂, ♀, JUV., OR IMM.	SPECIES	SIGHTED (DATE)	AT (PLACE)

SPECIES	SIGHTED (DATE)	AT (PLACE)	♂, ♀, JUV., OR IMM.

The Fall Weekend Warbler Watch

DATE

. . . .

PLACE

. . . .

SPECIES SIGHTED

. . . .

NUMBER

SIGHTINGS OF WOOD WARBLERS

Subfamily Parulinae

♂	♀	JUV.	IMM.	GENUS *Vermivora*
—	—	—	—	Orange-crowned Warbler, *Vermivora celata*
—	—	—	—	Nashville Warbler, *Vermivora ruficapilla*
—	—	—	—	Virginia's Warbler (S), *Vermivora virginiae*
—	—	—	—	Lucy's Warbler (S), *Vermivora luciae*
				GENUS *Dendroica*
—	—	—	—	Yellow Warbler, *Dendroica petechia*
—	—	—	—	Yellow-rumped Warbler, *Dendroica coronata*
—	—	—	—	Black-throated Gray Warbler, *Dendroica nigrescens*
—	—	—	—	Townsend's Warbler, *Dendroica townsendi*
—	—	—	—	Hermit Warbler (W), *Dendroica occidentalis*

	♂	♀	JUV.	IMM.

Grace's Warbler (S),
Dendroica graciae

GENUS *Mniotilta*

Black-and-white Warbler,
Mniotilta varia

GENUS *Setophaga*

American Redstart, *Setophaga
ruticilla*

GENUS *Seiurus*

Ovenbird, *Seiurus aurocapillus*

Northern Waterthrush, *Seiurus
noveboracensis*

GENUS *Geothlypis*

Common Yellowthroat,
Geothlypsis trichas

GENUS *Wilsonia*

Wilson's Warbler, *Wilsonia
pusilla*

GENUS *Cardellina*

Red-faced Warbler (SW),
Cardellina rubrifrons

GENUS *Myioborus*

Painted Redstart (SW),
Myioborus pictus

GENUS *Icteria*

Yellow-breasted Chat, *Icteria
virens*

GENUS *Peucedramus*

Olive Warbler (SW),
Peucedramus taeniatus

S P E C I E S   S I G H T E D

(Fill in ♂, ♀, Juv., or Imm.)

P I G E O N S ,   D O V E S ,   A N D
R O A D R U N N E R S

_____ Band-tailed Pigeon, *Columba fasciata*

_____ Mourning Dove, *Zenaida macroura*

_____ Greater Roadrunner (S),
Geococcyx californianus

BEGINNING ON

. . . .

D   A   T   E

AND
ENDING ON

. . . .

D   A   T   E

AT

. . . .

P   L   A   C   E

O W L S

_____ Common Barn-Owl, *Tyto alba*

_____ Flammulated Owl, *Otus flammeolus*

_____ Western Screech-Owl, *Otus kennicottii*

_____ Great Horned Owl, *Bubo virginianus*

_____ Snowy Owl (N), *Nyctea scandiaca*

_____ Northern Hawk-Owl (N), *Surnia ulula*

_____ Burrowing Owl, *Athene cunicularia*

_____ Spotted Owl, *Strix occidentalis*

_____ Barred Owl (N), *Strix varia*

_____ Great Gray Owl (N), *Strix nebulosa*

_____ Long-eared Owl, *Asio otus*

_____ Short-eared Owl, *Asio flammeus*

_____ Boreal Owl (N), *Aegolius funereus*

_____ Northern Saw-whet Owl, *Aegolius acadicus*

H U M M I N G B I R D S

_____ Anna's Hummingbird (W), *Calypte anna*

K I N G F I S H E R S ,
W O O D P E C K E R S ,
A N D   A L L I E S

_____ Belted Kingfisher (W, S), *Ceryle alcyon*

_____ Lewis' Woodpecker (W, S), *Melanerpes lewis*

Acorn Woodpecker (S), *Melanerpes formicivorus* _____

Yellow-bellied Sapsucker, *Sphyrapicus varius* _____

Red-naped Sapsucker, *Sphyrapicus nuchalis* _____

Red-breasted Sapsucker (W), *Sphyrapicus ruber* _____

Williamson's Sapsucker (S), *Sphyrapicus thyroideus* _____

Nuttall's Woodpecker (W), *Picoides nuttallii* _____

Downy Woodpecker, *Picoides pubescens* _____

Hairy Woodpecker, *Picoides villosus* _____

White-headed Woodpecker (W), *Picoides albolarvatus* _____

Northern Flicker, *Colaptes auratus* _____

Pileated Woodpecker (N), *Dryocopus pileatus* _____

FLYCATCHERS, LARKS, AND SWALLOWS

Black Phoebe (SW), *Sayornis nigricans* _____

Say's Phoebe (S), *Sayornis saya* _____

_____ Horned Lark, *Eremophila alpestris*
_____ Tree Swallow (S), *Tachycineta bicolor*

JAYS, MAGPIES, AND CROWS

_____ Gray Jay (N), *Perisoreus canadensis*
_____ Steller's Jay, *Cyanocitta stelleri*
_____ Scrub Jay (S), *Aphelocoma coerulescens*
_____ Clark's Nutcracker, *Nucifraga columbiana*
_____ Black-billed Magpie, *Pica pica*
_____ American Crow, *Corvus brachyrhynchos*
_____ Northwestern Crow, *Corvus caurinus*
_____ Common Raven, *Corvus corax*

CHICKADEES, TITMICE, AND ALLIES

_____ Black-capped Chickadee (N), *Parus atricapillus*
_____ Mountain Chickadee, *Parus gambeli*
_____ Boreal Chickadee (N), *Parus hudsonicus*
_____ Chestnut-backed Chickadee (W), *Parus rufescens*
_____ Bridled Titmouse (S), *Parus wollweberi*
_____ Plain Titmouse, *Parus inornatus*
_____ Verdin (SW), *Auriparus flaviceps*
_____ Bushtit, *Psaltriparus minimus*

NUTHATCHES, CREEPERS, AND DIPPERS

_____ Red-breasted Nuthatch, *Sitta candensis*
_____ White-breasted Nuthatch, *Sitta carolinensis*
_____ Pygmy Nuthatch, *Sitta pygmaea*
_____ Brown Creeper, *Certhia americana*
_____ American Dipper, *Cinclus mexicanus*

KINGLETS, GNATCATCHERS, SOLITAIRES, THRUSHES, AND ALLIES

Golden-crowned Kinglet, *Regulus satrapa* ———

Ruby-crowned Kinglet (S), *Regulus calendula* ———

Blue-gray Gnatcatcher (S), *Polioptila caerulea* ———

Western Bluebird (SW), *Sialia mexicana* ———

Mountain Bluebird (SW), *Sialia currucoides* ———

Townsend's Solitaire, *Myadestes townsendi* ———

Hermit Thrush (W, S), *Catharus guttatus* ———

American Robin, *Turdus migratorius* ———

Varied Thrush (W), *Ixoreus naevius* ———

Wrentit (W), *Chamaea fasciata* ———

MOCKINGBIRDS, THRASHERS, AND PIPITS

Northern Mockingbird (S), *Mimus polyglottos* ———

Sage Thrasher (SW), *Oreoscoptes montanus* ———

Bendire's Thrasher (S), *Toxostoma bendirei* ———

Curve-billed Thrasher (S), *Toxostoma curvirostre* ———

California Thrasher (SW), *Toxostoma redivivum* ———

Crissal Thrasher (S), *Toxostoma dorsale* ———

LeConte's Thrasher (SW), *Toxostoma lecontei* ———

Water Pipit (W, S), *Anthus spinoletta* ———

WAXWINGS, SHRIKES, STARLINGS, AND VIREOS

Bohemian Waxwing (N), *Bombycilla garrulus* ———

Cedar Waxwing, *Bombycilla cedrorum* ———

Northern Shrike, *Lanius excubitor* ———

Loggerhead Shrike (S), *Lanius ludovicianus* ———

_____ European Starling, *Sturnus vulgaris*

_____ Hutton's Vireo (W), *Vireo huttoni*

WARBLERS

_____ Orange-crowned Warbler (W), *Vermivora celata*

_____ Yellow-rumped Warbler (W, S), *Dendroica coronata*

_____ Townsend's Warbler (W), *Dendroica townsendi*

_____ Common Yellowthroat (S), *Geothlypis trichas*

TOWHEES, SPARROWS, AND ALLIES

_____ Rufous-sided Towhee, *Pipilo erythrophthalmus*

_____ Brown Towhee (W, S), *Pipilo fuscus*

_____ Rufous-crowned Sparrow (S), *Aimophila ruficeps*

_____ American Tree Sparrow, *Spizella arborea*

_____ Chipping Sparrow (S), *Spizella passerina*

_____ Brewer's Sparrow (S), *Spizella breweri*

_____ Vesper Sparrow (S), *Pooecetes gramineus*

_____ Lark Sparrow (S), *Chondestes grammacus*

_____ Black-throated Sparrow (SW), *Amphispiza bilineata*

_____ Sage Sparrow (S), *Amphispiza belli*

_____ Lark Bunting, *Calamospiza melanocorys*

_____ Fox Sparrow (W, S), *Passerella iliaca*

_____ Song Sparrow, *Melospiza melodia*

_____ Lincoln's Sparrow (W, S), *Melospiza lincolnii*

_____ Golden-crowned Sparrow (W), *Zonotrichia atricapilla*

_____ White-crowned Sparrow, *Zonotrichia leucophrys*

_____ Harris' Sparrow (SE), *Zonotrichia querula*

Dark-eyed Junco, *Junco hyemalis* ⎯⎯⎯

McCown's Longspur (S), *Calcarius mccownii* ⎯⎯⎯

Lapland Longspur, *Calcarius lapponicus* ⎯⎯⎯

Chestnut-collared Longspur (S), *Calcarius ornatus* ⎯⎯⎯

Snow Bunting (N), *Plectrophenax nivalis* ⎯⎯⎯

MEADOWLARKS AND BLACKBIRDS

Red-winged Blackbird, *Agelaius phoeniceus* ⎯⎯⎯

Tricolored Blackbird (W), *Agelaius tricolor* ⎯⎯⎯

Western Meadowlark, *Sturnella neglecta* ⎯⎯⎯

Yellow-headed Blackbird (SW), *Xanthocephalus xanthocephalus* ⎯⎯⎯

Brewer's Blackbird, *Euphagus cyanocephalus* ⎯⎯⎯

Great-tailed Grackle (S), *Quiscalus mexicanus* ⎯⎯⎯

Brown-headed Cowbird (S), *Molothrus ater* ⎯⎯⎯

FINCHES AND ALLIES

Rosy Finch, *Leucosticte arctoa* ⎯⎯⎯

Pine Grosbeak (N, E), *Pinicola enucleator* ⎯⎯⎯

Purple Finch (W), *Carpodacus purpureus* ⎯⎯⎯

Cassin's Finch, *Carpodacus cassinii* ⎯⎯⎯

House Finch, *Carpodacus mexicanus* ⎯⎯⎯

Red Crossbill, *Loxia curvirostra* ⎯⎯⎯

White-winged Crossbill (N), *Loxia leucoptera* ⎯⎯⎯

Common Redpoll (N), *Carduelis flammea* ⎯⎯⎯

Pine Siskin, *Carduelis pinus* ⎯⎯⎯

Lesser Goldfinch (SW), *Carduelis psaltria* ⎯⎯⎯

Lawrence's Goldfinch, *Carduelis lawrencei* ⎯⎯⎯

American Goldfinch, *Carduelis tristis* ⎯⎯⎯

Evening Grosbeak, *Coccothraustes verpertinus* ⎯⎯⎯

House Sparrow, *Passer domesticus* ⎯⎯⎯

Desert Southwest Species

SPECIES SIGHTED

♂	♀	JUV.	IMM.	HAWKS
—	—	—	—	Common Black-Hawk, *Buteogallus anthracinus*
—	—	—	—	Harris' Hawk, *Parabuteo unicinctus*
—	—	—	—	Gray Hawk, *Buteo nitidus*
—	—	—	—	Zone-tailed Hawk, *Buteo albonotatus*

DATE

. . . .

				QUAIL AND DOVES
—	—	—	—	Montezuma Quail, *Cyrtonyx montezumae*
—	—	—	—	Scaled Quail, *Callipepla squamata*
—	—	—	—	Gambel's Quail, *Callipepla gambelii*

PLACE

. . . .

SPECIES SIGHTED

. . . .

NUMBER

	♂	♀	JUV.	IMM.

White-winged Dove, *Zenaida asiatica* — — — —

Inca Dove, *Columbina inca* — — — —

OWLS AND GOATSUCKERS

. . . .

Whiskered Screech-Owl, *Otus trichopsis* — — —

Ferruginous Pygmy-Owl, *Glaudicium brasilianum* — — —

Elf Owl, *Micrathene whitneyi* — — —

Lesser Nighthawk, *Chordeiles acutipennis* — — —

HUMMINGBIRDS

Blue-throated Hummingbird, *Lampornis clemenciae* — — —

Magnificent Hummingbird, *Eugenes fulgens* — — —

Costa's Hummingbird, *Calypte costae* — — —

TROGONS AND WOODPECKERS

Elegant Trogon, *Trogon elegans* — — —

Gila Woodpecker, *Melanerpes uropygialis* — — —

Ladder-backed Woodpecker, *Picoides scalaris* — — —

Strickland's Woodpecker, *Picoides stricklandi* — —

FLYCATCHERS AND JAYS

Greater Pewee, *Contopus pertinax* — — —

Vermilion Flycatcher, *Pyrocephalus rubinus* — — —

Ash-throated Flycatcher, *Myiarchus cinerascens* — — —

♂	♀	JUV.	IMM.	
—	—	—	—	Ash-throated Flycatcher, *Myiarchus cinerascens*
—	—	—	—	Brown-crested Flycatcher, *Myiarchus tyrannulus*
—	—	—	—	Sulphur-bellied Flycatcher, *Myiodynastes luteiventris*
—	—	—	—	Rose-throated Becard, *Pachyramphus aglaiae*
—	—	—	—	Gray-breasted Jay, *Aphelocoma ultramarinia*

CHICKADEES, TITMICE, AND ALLIES

♂	♀	JUV.	IMM.	
—	—	—	—	Mexican Chickadee, *Parus sclateri*
—	—	—	—	Bridled Titmouse, *Parus wollweberi*
—	—	—	—	Verdin, *Auriparus flaviceps*

WRENS AND GNATCATCHERS

♂	♀	JUV.	IMM.	
—	—	—	—	Cactus Wren, *Campylorhynchus brunneicapilus*
—	—	—	—	Black-tailed Gnatcatcher, *Polioptila melanura*

THRASHERS AND PHAINOPEPLA

♂	♀	JUV.	IMM.	
—	—	—	—	Bendire's Thrasher, *Toxostoma bendirei*
—	—	—	—	Curve-billed Thrasher, *Toxostoma curvirostre*
—	—	—	—	California Thrasher, *Toxostoma redivivum*
—	—	—	—	Crissal Thrasher, *Toxostoma dorsale*
—	—	—	—	Phainopepla, *Phainopepla nitens*

WARBLERS	♂	♀	JUV.	IMM.
Lucy's Warbler, *Vermivora luciae*	___	___	___	___
Grace's Warbler, *Dendroica graciae*	___	___	___	___
Red-faced Warbler, *Cardellina rubrifrons*	___	___	___	___
Painted Redstart, *Myioborus pictus*	___	___	___	___
Olive Warbler, *Peucedramus taeniatus*	___	___	___	___

TANAGERS, CARDINALS, AND GROSBEAKS

	♂	♀	JUV.	IMM.
Hepatic Tanager, *Piranga flava*	___	___	___	___
Summer Tanager, *Piranga rubra*	___	___	___	___
Pyrrhuloxia, *Cardinalis sinuatus*	___	___	___	___
Varied Bunting, *Passerina versicolor*	___	___	___	___

TOWHEES, SPARROWS, AND ALLIES

	♂	♀	JUV.	IMM.
Abert's Towhee, *Pipilo aberti*	___	___	___	___
Botteri's Sparrow, *Aimophila botterii*	___	___	___	___
Cassin's Sparrow, *Aimophila cassinii*	___	___	___	___
Rufous-winged Sparrow, *Aimophila carpalis*	___	___	___	___
Yellow-eyed Junco, *Junco phaeonotus*	___	___	___	___

BLACKBIRDS

	♂	♀	JUV.	IMM.
Brown-headed Cowbird, *Molothrus ater*	___	___	___	___

Permanent Residents

BEGINNING ON

. . . .

D A T E

**AND
ENDING ON**

. . . .

D A T E

FOR

. . . .

Y E A R

AT

. . . .

P L A C E

S P E C I E S   S I G H T E D

(Fill in ♂, ♀, Juv., or Imm.)

P E L I C A N S ,   C O R M O R A N T S
A N D   H E R O N S

———— Brown Pelican (W), *Pelecanus occidentalis*

———— Brandt's Cormorant (W), *Phalacrocorax penicillatus*

———— Pelagic Cormorant (W), *Phalacrocorax pelagicus*

———— Great Blue Heron, *Ardea herodias*

E A G L E S ,   H A W K S ,   A N D
F A L C O N S

———— Northern Goshawk, *Accipiter gentilis*

———— Harris' Hawk (SW), *Parabuteo unicinctus*

———— Red-shouldered Hawk (S), *Buteo lineatus*

———— Red-tailed Hawk (S), *Buteo jamaicensis*

———— Golden Eagle, *Aquila chrysaetos*

———— American Kestrel, *Falco sparverius*

PARTRIDGES, GROUSE, TURKEYS, AND QUAIL

Gray Partridge (N). *Perdix perdix* _____

Chukar, *Alectoris chukar* _____

Ring-necked Pheasant (N), *Phasianus colchicus* _____

Spruce Grouse (N), *Dendragapus canadensis* _____

Blue Grouse, *Dendragapus obscurus* _____

White-tailed Ptarmigan (N, E), *Lagopus leucurus* _____

Ruffed Grouse (N), *Bonasa umbellus* _____

Sage Grouse, *Centrocercus urophasianus* _____

Lesser Prairie-Chicken (SE), *Tympanuchus pallidicinctus* _____

Sharp-tailed Grouse (NE), *Tympanuchus phasianellus* _____

Wild Turkey (S), *Meleagris gallopavo* _____

Montezuma Quail (S), *Crytonyx montezumae* _____

Scaled Quail (SE), *Callipepla squamata* _____

Gambel's Quail (S), *Callipepla gambelii* _____

California Quail (W), *Callipepla californica* _____

Mountain Quail (W), *Oreortyx pictus* _____

GALLINULES

Common Moorhen (S), *Gallinula chloropus* _____

OYSTERCATCHERS

American Black Oystercatcher (N), *Haematopus bachmani* _____

GULLS

Western Gull (W), *Larus occidentalis* _____

MURRES AND PUFFINS

Common Murre (W), *Uria aalge* _____

Pigeon Guillemot (W), *Cepphus columba* _____

_____ Marbled Murrelet (W), *Brachyramphus marmoratus*

_____ Rhinoceros Auklet (W), *Cerorhinca monocerata*

_____ Tufted Puffin (W), *Fratercula cirrhata*

PIGEONS, DOVES, AND ALLIES

_____ Rock Dove, *Columba livia*

_____ Band-tailed Pigeon, *Columba fasciata*

_____ Mourning Dove, *Zenaida macroura*

_____ Inca Dove (SW), *Columbina inca*

_____ Common Ground-Dove, *Columbina passerina*

_____ Greater Roadrunner (S), *Geococcyx californianus*

OWLS

_____ Common Barn-Owl, *Tyto alba*

_____ Western Screech-Owl, *Otus kennicottii*

_____ Northern Pygmy-Owl, *Glaucidium gnoma*

_____ Spotted Owl, *Strix occidentalis*

_____ Great Gray Owl (N), *Strix nebulosa*

_____ Long-eared Owl, *Asio otus*

_____ Boreal Owl (N), *Aegolius funereus*

_____ Northern Saw-whet Owl (N), *Aegolius acadicus*

WOODPECKERS

_____ Acorn Woodpecker (W), *Melanerpes formicivorus*

_____ Gila Woodpecker (S), *Melanerpes uropygialis*

_____ Red-breasted Sapsucker (NW), *Sphyrapicus ruber*

_____ Ladder-backed Woodpecker (S), *Picoides scalaris*

_____ Nuttall's Woodpecker (W), *Picoides nuttallii*

Downy Woodpecker, *Picoides pubescens* _____

Hairy Woodpecker, *Picoides villosus* _____

Strickland's Woodpecker (SW), *Picoides stricklandi* _____

White-headed Woodpecker (W), *Picoides albolarvatus* _____

Three-toed Woodpecker (N), *Picoides tridactylus* _____

Black-backed Woodpecker (N), *Picoides arcticus* _____

Pileated Woodpecker (N), *Dryocopus pileatus* _____

LARKS

Horned Lark, *Eremophila alpestris* _____

JAYS, MAGPIES, AND CROWS

Gray Jay (N), *Perisoreus canadensis* _____

Steller's Jay, *Cyanocitta stelleri* _____

Scrub Jay (S), *Aphelocoma coerulescens* _____

Pinyon Jay, *Gymnorhinus cyanocephalus* _____

Clark's Nutcracker, *Nucifraga columbiana* _____

Black-billed Magpie, *Pica pica* _____

American Crow, *Corvus brachyrhynchos* _____

Northwestern Crow (NW), *Corvus caurinus* _____

Chihuahuan Raven (S), *Corvus cryptoleucus* _____

Common Raven, *Corvus corax* _____

CHICKADEES, TITMICE, AND ALLIES

Black-capped Chickadee (N), *Parus atricapillus* _____

Mexican Chickadee (SW), *Parus sclateri* _____

Mountain Chickadee, *Parus gambeli* _____

Boreal Chickadee (N), *Parus hudsonicus* _____

Chestnut-backed Chickadee (W), *Parus rufescens* _____

_____ Bridled Titmouse (SW), *Parus wollweberi*

_____ Plain Titmouse, *Parus inornatus*

_____ Verdin (S), *Auriparus flaviceps*

_____ Bushtit (S), *Psaltriparus minimus*

NUTHATCHES, CREEPERS, WRENS, AND DIPPERS

_____ White-breasted Nuthatch, *Sitta carolinensis*

_____ Pygmy Nuthatch, *Sitta pygmaea*

_____ Brown Creeper, *Certhia americana*

_____ Cactus Wren (S), *Campylorhynchus brunneicapilus*

_____ Canyon Wren, *Catherpes mexicanus*

_____ Bewick's Wren (S), *Thryomanes bewickii*

_____ American Dipper, *Cinclus mexicanus*

GNATCATCHERS AND ALLIES

_____ Black-tailed Gnatcatcher (S), *Polioptila melanura*

_____ Wrentit (W), *Chamaea fasciata*

MOCKINGBIRDS AND THRASHERS

_____ Northern Mockingbird (S), *Mimus polyglottos*

_____ Curve-billed Thrasher (S), *Toxostoma curvirostre*

_____ California Thrasher (W), *Toxostoma redivivum*

_____ Crissal Thrasher (SW), *Toxostoma dorsale*

_____ LeConte's Thrasher (SW), *Toxostoma lecontei*

STARLINGS AND VIREOS

_____ European Starling, *Sturnus vulgaris*

_____ Hutton's Vireo (W), *Vireo huttoni*

CARDINALS

Northern Cardinal (S), *Cardinalis cardinalis* _____

Pyrrhuloxia (S), *Cardinalis sinuatus* _____

TOWHEES, SPARROWS, AND ALLIES

Brown Towhee (S), *Pipilo fuscus* _____

Abert's Towhee (SW), *Pipilo aberti* _____

Rufous-winged Sparrow (SW), *Aimophila carpalis* _____

Rufous-crowned Sparrow (S), *Aimophila ruficeps* _____

Dark-eyed Junco, *Junco hyemalis* _____

Yellow-eyed Junco (S), *Junco phaeonotus* _____

BLACKBIRDS

Red-winged Blackbird, *Agelaius phoeniceus* _____

Tricolored Blackbird (W), *Agelaius tricolor* _____

FINCHES AND ALLIES

Purple Finch (W), *Carpodacus purpureus* _____

House Finch, *Carpodacus mexicanus* _____

House Sparrow, *Passer domesticus* _____

Hawaiian Specialties

DATE

. . . .

PLACE

. . . .

SPECIES SIGHTED

. . . .

NUMBER

NATIVE SPECIES

_____ Apapane, *Himatione sanguinea*

_____ Common Amakihi, *Hemignathus virens*

_____ Elepaio, *Chasiempis sandwichensis*

_____ Hawaiian Creeper, *Oreomystis mana*

_____ Hawaiian Crow, *Corvus tropicus*

_____ Hawaiian Duck, *Anas wyvilliana*

_____ Hawaiian Hawk, *Buteo solitarius*

_____ Hawaiian Thrush, *Phaeornis obscurus*

_____ Iiwi, *Vestiaria coccinea*

_____ Kauai Creeper, *Oreomystis bairdi*

_____ Maui Creeper, *Paroreomyza montana*

_____ Nene, *Branta sandvicensis*

_____ Palila, *Loxioides bailleui*

INTRODUCED EXOTICS

Vagrant
Species

COMMENTS	SPECIES SIGHTED (DATE)	AT (PLACE)

SPECIES	SIGHTED (DATE)	AT (PLACE)	COMMENTS

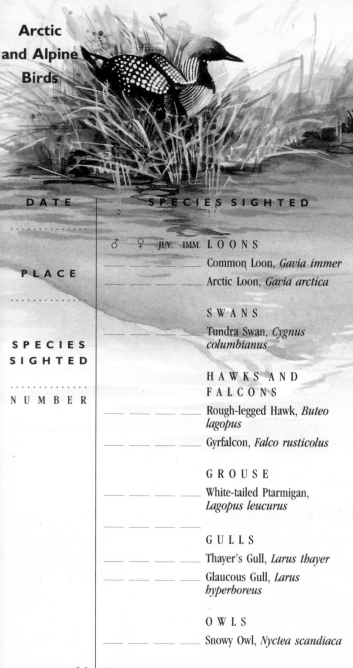

Arctic and Alpine Birds

DATE

....

PLACE

....

SPECIES SIGHTED

....

NUMBER

♂	♀	JUV.	IMM.	**LOONS**

SPECIES SIGHTED

♂	♀	JUV.	IMM.	
—	—	—	—	Common Loon, *Gavia immer*
—	—	—	—	Arctic Loon, *Gavia arctica*

SWANS

| — | — | — | — | Tundra Swan, *Cygnus columbianus* |

HAWKS AND FALCONS

| — | — | — | — | Rough-legged Hawk, *Buteo lagopus* |
| — | — | — | — | Gyrfalcon, *Falco rusticolus* |

GROUSE

| — | — | — | — | White-tailed Ptarmigan, *Lagopus leucurus* |

GULLS

| — | — | — | — | Thayer's Gull, *Larus thayer* |
| — | — | — | — | Glaucous Gull, *Larus hyperboreus* |

OWLS

| — | — | — | — | Snowy Owl, *Nyctea scandiaca* |

SHRIKES

	♂	♀	JUV.	IMM.
Northern Shrike, *Lanius excubitor*	—	—	—	—

SPARROWS AND ALLIES

Harris' Sparrow, *Zonotrichia querula*	—	—	—	—
Lapland Longspur, *Calcarius lapponicus*	—	—	—	—
Snow Bunting, *Plectrophenax nivalis*	—	—	—	—

FINCHES AND ALLIES

| Rosy Finch, *Leucosticte arctoa* | — | — | — | — |
| Common Redpoll, *Carduelis flammea* | — | — | — | — |

North American Travel List

SPECIES	SIGHTED (DATE)	AT (PLACE)

SPECIES	SIGHTED (DATE)	AT (PLACE)	COMMENTS AND SIGHTING NOTES
			. . . .

World
Travel
List

SPECIES	SIGHTED (DATE)	AT (PLACE)

SPECIES	SIGHTED (DATE)	AT (PLACE)	COMMENTS AND SIGHTING NOTES
			. . . .

The Life List

♂	♀	Juv.	Imm.	**LOONS AND GREBES**
—	—	—	—	Red-throated Loon, *Gavia stellata*
—	—	—	—	Arctic Loon, *Gavia arctica*
—	—	—	—	Common Loon, *Gavia immer*
—	—	—	—	Least Grebe, *Tachybaptus dominicus*
—	—	—	—	Pied-billed Grebe, *Podilymbus podiceps*
—	—	—	—	Horned Grebe, *Podiceps auritus*
—	—	—	—	Red-necked Grebe, *Podiceps grisegena*
—	—	—	—	Eared Grebe, *Podiceps nigricollis*
—	—	—	—	Western Grebe, *Aechmophorus occidentalis*

♂	♀	Juv.	Imm.	**ALBATROSSES, SHEARWATERS, AND PETRELS**
—	—	—	—	Black-footed Albatross, *Diomedea nigripes*
—	—	—	—	Northern Fulmar, *Fulmarus glacialis*
—	—	—	—	Pink-footed Shearwater, *Puffinus creatopus*
—	—	—	—	Sooty Shearwater, *Puffinus griseus*
—	—	—	—	Manx Shearwater, *Puffinus puffinus*
—	—	—	—	Fork-tailed Storm-Petrel, *Oceanodroma furcata*
—	—	—	—	Leach's Storm-Petrel, *Oceanodroma leucorhoa*

	♂	♀	Juv.	Imm.

Ashy Storm-Petrel, _Oceanodroma homochroa_ — — — —

Black Storm-Petrel, _Oceanodroma melania_ — — — —

B O O B I E S, P E L I C A N S, C O R M O R A N T S, D A R T E R S, A N D F R I G A T E B I R D S

Blue-footed Booby, _Sula nebouxii_ — — — —

American White Pelican, _Pelecanus erythrorhynchos_ — — — —

Brown Pelican, _Pelecanus occidentalis_ — — — —

Double-crested Cormorant, _Phalacrocorax auritus_ — — — —

Brandt's Cormorant, _Phalacrocorax penicillatus_ — — — —

Pelagic Cormorant, _Phalacrocorax pelagicus_ — — — —

Anhinga, _Anhinga anhinga_ — — — —

Magnificent Frigatebird, _Fregata magnificens_ — — — —

B I T T E R N S, H E R O N S, I B I S E S, A N D S T O R K S

American Bittern, _Botaurus lentiginosus_ — — — —

Least Bittern, _Ixobrychus exilis_

Great Blue Heron, _Ardea herodias_ — — — —

Great Egret, _Casmerodius albus_ — — — —

Snowy Egret, _Egretta thula_ — — — —

Little Blue Heron, _Egretta caerulea_ — — — —

Reddish Egret, _Egretta rufescens_

Cattle Egret, _Bubulcus ibis_ — — — —

Green-backed Heron, _Butorides striatus_ — — — —

Black-crowned Night Heron, _Nycticorax nycticorax_ — — — —

Yellow-crowned Night-Heron, _Nycticorax violaceus_ — — — —

White-faced Ibis, _Plegadis chihi_ — — — —

Wood Stork, _Mycteria americana_ — — — —

S W A N S, G E E S E, A N D D U C K S

Fulvous Whistling-Duck, _Dendrocygna bicolor_ — — — —

Tundra Swan, _Cygnus columbianus_ — — — —

Trumpeter Swan, _Cygnus buccinator_ — — — —

_____ Greater White-fronted Goose, *Anser albifrons*

_____ Snow Goose, *Chen caerulescens*

_____ Ross' Goose, *Chen rossii*

_____ Brant, *Branta bernicla*

_____ Canada Goose, *Branta canadensis*

_____ Wood Duck, *Aix sponsa*

_____ Green-winged Teal, *Anas crecca*

_____ Mallard, *Anas platyrhynchos*

_____ Northern Pintail, *Anas acuta*

_____ Blue-winged Teal, *Anas discors*

_____ Cinnamon Teal, *Anas cyanoptera*

_____ Northern Shoveler, *Anas clypeata*

_____ Gadwall, *Anas strepera*

_____ Eurasian Wigeon, *Anas penelope*

_____ American Wigeon, *Anas americana*

_____ Canvasback, *Aythya valisineria*

_____ Redhead, *Aythya americana*

_____ Ring-necked Duck, *Aythya collaris*

_____ Greater Scaup, *Aythya marila*

_____ Lesser Scaup, *Aythya affinis*

_____ King Eider, *Somateria spectabilis*

_____ Harlequin Duck, *Histrionicus histrionicus*

_____ Oldsquaw, *Clangula hyemalis*

_____ Black Scoter, *Melanitta nigra*

_____ Surf Scoter, *Melanitta perspicillata*

_____ White-winged Scoter, *Melanitta fusca*

_____ Common Goldeneye, *Bucephala clangula*

_____ Barrow's Goldeneye, *Bucephala islandica*

_____ Bufflehead, *Bucephala albeola*

_____ Hooded Merganser, *Lophodytes cucullatus*

_____ Common Merganser, *Mergus merganser*

_____ Red-breasted Merganser, *Mergus serrator*

_____ Ruddy Duck, *Oxyura jamaicensis*

VULTURES   ♂ ♀ Juv. Imm.

Black Vulture, ____ ____ ____ ____
Coragyps atratus

Turkey Vulture, ____ ____ ____ ____
Cathartes aura

California Condor, ____ ____ ____ ____
*Gymnogyps
californianus*

KITES,
EAGLES,
HAWKS, AND
ALLIES

Osprey, *Pandion* ____ ____ ____ ____
haliaetus

Black-shouldered ____ ____ ____ ____
Kite, *Elanus
caeruleus*

Mississippi Kite, ____ ____ ____ ____
*Ictinia
mississippiensis*

Bald Eagle, ____ ____ ____ ____
*Haliaeetus
leucocephalus*

Northern Harrier, ____ ____ ____ ____
Circus cyaneus

Sharp-shinned ____ ____ ____ ____
Hawk, *Accipiter
striatus*

Cooper's Hawk, ____ ____ ____ ____
Accipiter cooperii

Northern Goshawk, ____ ____ ____ ____
Accipiter gentilis

Common Black- ____ ____ ____ ____
Hawk, *Buteogallus
anthracinus*

Harris' Hawk, ____ ____ ____ ____
*Parabuteo
unicinctus*

Gray Hawk, *Buteo* ____ ____ ____ ____
nitidus

   ♂ ♀ Juv. Imm.

Red-shouldered ____ ____ ____ ____
Hawk, *Buteo
lineatus*

Broad-winged ____ ____ ____ ____
Hawk, *Buteo
platypterus*

Swainson's Hawk, ____ ____ ____ ____
Buteo swainsoni

White-tailed Hawk, ____ ____ ____ ____
Buteo albicaudatus

Zone-tailed Hawk, ____ ____ ____ ____
Buteo albonotatus

Red-tailed Hawk, ____ ____ ____ ____
Buteo jamaicensis

Ferruginous Hawk, ____ ____ ____ ____
Buteo regalis

Rough-legged ____ ____ ____ ____
Hawk, *Buteo
lagopus*

Golden Eagle, ____ ____ ____ ____
Aquila chrysaetos

CARACARAS
AND FALCONS

Crested Caracara, ____ ____ ____ ____
Polyborus plancus

American Kestrel, ____ ____ ____ ____
Falco sparverius

Merlin, *Falco* ____ ____ ____ ____
columbarius

Peregrine Falcon, ____ ____ ____ ____
Falco peregrinus

Gyrfalcon, *Falco* ____ ____ ____ ____
rusticolus

Prairie Falcon, ____ ____ ____ ____
Falco mexicanus

♂	♀	Juv.	Imm.	
				CHACHALACA, PARTRIDGES, GROUSE, TURKEYS, AND QUAIL
—	—	—	—	Plain Chachalaca, *Ortalis vetula*
—	—	—	—	Gray Partridge, *Perdix perdix*
—	—	—	—	Chukar, *Alectoris chukar*
—	—	—	—	Ring-necked Pheasant, *Phasianus colchicus*
—	—	—	—	Spruce Grouse, *Dendragapus canadensis*
—	—	—	—	Blue Grouse, *Dendragapus obscurus*
—	—	—	—	Willow Ptarmigan, *Lagopus lagopus*
—	—	—	—	Rock Ptarmigan, *Lagopus mutus*
—	—	—	—	White-tailed Ptarmigan, *Lagopus leucurus*
—	—	—	—	Ruffed Grouse, *Bonasa umbellus*
—	—	—	—	Sage Grouse, *Centrocercus urophasianus*
—	—	—	—	Greater Prairie-Chicken, *Tympanuchus cupido*
—	♀	—	—	Lesser Prairie-Chicken, *Tympanuchus pallidicinctus*

♂	♀	Juv.	Imm.	
—	—	—	—	Sharp-tailed Grouse, *Tympanuchus phasianellus*
—	—	—	—	Wild Turkey, *Meleagris gallopavo*
—	—	—	—	Montezuma Quail, *Cyrtonyx montezumae*
—	—	—	—	Northern Bobwhite, *Colinus virginianus*
—	—	—	—	Scaled Quail, *Callipepla squamata*
—	—	—	—	Gambel's Quail, *Callipepla gambelii*
—	—	—	—	California Quail, *Callipepla californica*
—	—	—	—	Mountain Quail, *Oreortyx pictus*
				RAILS, GALLINULES, COOTS, AND CRANES
—	—	—	—	Yellow Rail, *Coturnicops noveboracensis*
—	—	—	—	Black Rail, *Laterallus jamaicensis*
—	—	—	—	Clapper Rail, *Rallus longirostris*
—	—	—	—	Virginia Rail, *Rallus limicola*
—	—	—	—	Sora, *Porzana carolina*
—	—	—	—	Common Moorhen, *Gallinula chloropus*

	♂	♀	Juv.	Imm.

American Coot, _____ _____ _____ _____
Fulica americana

Sandhill Crane, _____ _____ _____ _____
Grus canadensis

Whooping Crane, _____ _____ _____ _____
Grus americana

PLOVERS, AND OYSTERCATCHERS

Black-bellied _____ _____ _____ _____
Plover, *Pluvialis squatarola*

Snowy Plover, _____ _____ _____ _____
Charadrius alexandrinus

Semipalmated _____ _____ _____ _____
Plover, *Charadrius semipalmatus*

Piping Plover, _____ _____ _____ _____
Charadrius melodus

Killdeer, _____ _____ _____ _____
Charadrius vociferus

Mountain Plover, _____ _____ _____ _____
Charadrius montanus

American Black _____ _____ _____ _____
Oystercatcher,
Haematopus bachmani

STILTS, AVOCETS, SANDPIPERS, PHALAROPES, AND ALLIES

Black-necked Stilt, _____ _____ _____ _____
Himantopus mexicanus

American Avocet, _____ _____ _____ _____
Recurvirostra americana

	♂	♀	Juv.	Imm.

Greater Yellowlegs,
Tringa melanoleuca

Lesser Yellowlegs, _____ _____ _____ _____
Tringa flavipes

Solitary Sandpiper, _____ _____ _____ _____
Tringa solitaria

Willet, _____ _____ _____ _____
Catoptrophorus semipalmatus

Wandering Tattler, _____ _____ _____ _____
Heteroscelus incanus

Spotted Sandpiper, _____ _____ _____ _____
Actitis macularia

Upland Sandpiper, _____ _____ _____ _____
Bartramia longicauda

Whimbrel, _____ _____ _____ _____
Numenius phaeopus

Long-billed Curlew, _____ _____ _____ _____
Numenius americanus

Hudsonian Godwit, _____ _____ _____ _____
Limosa haemastica

Marbled Godwit, _____ _____ _____ _____
Limosa fedoa

Ruddy Turnstone, _____ _____ _____ _____
Arenaria interpres

Black Turnstone, _____ _____ _____ _____
Arenaria melanocephala

Surfbird, *Aphriza* _____ _____ _____ _____
virgata

Red Knot, *Calidris* _____ _____ _____ _____
canutus

Sanderling, *Calidris* _____ _____ _____ _____
alba

_____ Semipalmated Sandpiper, *Calidris pusilla*

_____ Western Sandpiper, *Calidris mauri*

_____ Least Sandpiper, *Calidris minutilla*

_____ White-rumped Sandpiper, *Calidris fuscicollis*

_____ Baird's Sandpiper, *Calidris bairdii*

_____ Pectoral Sandpiper, *Calidris melanotos*

_____ Rock Sandpiper, *Calidris ptilocnemis*

_____ Dunlin, *Calidris alpina*

_____ Stilt Sandpiper, *Calidris himantopus*

_____ Buff-breasted Sandpiper, *Tryngites subruficollis*

_____ Short-billed Dowitcher, *Limnodromus griseus*

_____ Long-billed Dowitcher, *Limnodromus scolopaceus*

_____ Common Snipe, *Gallinago gallinago*

_____ Wilson's Phalarope, *Phalaropus tricolor*

_____ Red-necked Phalarope, *Phalaropus lobatus*

_____ Red Phalarope, *Phalaropus fulicaria*

SKUAS, GULLS, TERNS, AND SKIMMERS

_____ Pomarine Jaeger, *Stercorarius pomarinus*

_____ Parasitic Jaeger, *Stercorarius parasiticus*

_____ Long-tailed Jaeger, *Stercorarius longicaudus*

_____ Franklin's Gull, *Larus pipixcan*

_____ Bonaparte's Gull, *Larus philadelphia*

_____ Heermann's Gull, *Larus heermanni*

_____ Mew Gull, *Larus canus*

_____ Ring-billed Gull, *Larus delawarensis*

_____ California Gull, *Larus californicus*

_____ Herring Gull, *Larus argentatus*

_____ Thayer's Gull, *Larus thayeri*

_____ Western Gull, *Larus occidentalis*

_____ Glaucous-winged Gull, *Larus glaucescens*

_____ Glaucous Gull, *Larus hyperboreus*

	♂	♀	Juv.	Imm.
Black-legged Kittiwake, *Rissa tridactyla*	—	—		
Sabine's Gull, *Xema sabini*	—	—	—	
Gull-billed Tern, *Sterna nilotica*	—	—	—	
Caspian Tern, *Sterna caspia*	—	—	—	
Royal Tern, *Sterna maxima*	—	—	—	
Elegant Tern, *Sterna elegans*	—	—	—	
Common Tern, *Sterna hirundo*	—	—	—	
Arctic Tern, *Sterna paradisaea*	—	—	—	
Forster's Tern, *Sterna forsteri*	—	—	—	
Least Tern, *Sterna antillarum*	—	—	—	
Black Tern, *Chlidonias niger*	—	—	—	
Black Skimmer, *Rynchops niger*	—	—	—	

AUKS, MURRES, AND PUFFINS

	♂	♀	Juv.	Imm.
Common Murre, *Uria aalge*	—	—	—	
Thick-billed Murre, *Uria lomvia*	—	—	—	—
Pigeon Guillemot, *Cepphus columba*	—	—	—	
Marbled Murrelet, *Brachyramphus marmoratus*	—	—	—	
Xantus' Murrelet, *Synthliboramphus hypoleucus*	—	—	—	

	♂	♀	Juv.	Imm.
Ancient Murrelet, *Synthliboramphus antiquus*	—	—		
Cassin's Auklet, *Ptychoramphus aleuticus*	—	—		
Parakeet Auklet, *Cyclorrhynchus psittacula*	—	—	—	
Crested Auklet, *Aethia cristatella*	—	—	—	
Rhinoceros Auklet, *Cerorhinca monocerata*	—	—	—	
Tufted Puffin, *Fratercula cirrhata*	—	—	—	
Horned Puffin, *Fratercula corniculata*	—	—	—	

PIGEONS, DOVES, CUCKOOS, AND ALLIES

	♂	♀	Juv.	Imm.
Rock Dove, *Columba livia*	—	—	—	
Band-tailed Pigeon, *Columba fasciata*	—	—	—	
Spotted Dove, *Streptopelia chinensis*	—	—	—	
White-winged Dove, *Zenaida asiatica*	—	—	—	
Mourning Dove, *Zenaida macroura*	—	—	—	
Inca Dove, *Columbina inca*	—	—	—	
Common Ground-Dove, *Columbina passerina*	—	—	—	

_ _ _ _ Black-billed Cuckoo, *Coccyzus erythropthalmus*

_ _ _ _ Yellow-billed Cuckoo, *Coccyzus americanus*

_ _ _ _ Greater Roadrunner, *Geococcyx californianus*

_ _ _ _ Groove-billed Ani, *Crotophaga sulcirostris*

OWLS

_ _ _ _ Common Barn-Owl, *Tyto alba*

_ _ _ _ Flammulated Owl, *Otus flammeolus*

_ _ _ _ Western Screech-Owl, *Otus kennicottii*

_ _ _ _ Whiskered Screech-Owl, *Otus trichopsis*

_ _ _ _ Great Horned Owl, *Bubo virginianus*

_ _ _ _ Snowy Owl, *Nyctea scandiaca*

_ _ _ _ Northern Hawk-Owl, *Surnia ulula*

_ _ _ _ Northern Pygmy-Owl, *Glaucidium gnoma*

_ _ _ _ Ferruginous Pygmy-Owl, *Glaudicium brasilianum*

_ _ _ _ Elf Owl, *Micrathene whitneyi*

_ _ _ _ Burrowing Owl, *Athene cunicularia*

_ _ _ _ Spotted Owl, *Strix occidentalis*

_ _ _ _ Barred Owl, *Strix varia*

_ _ _ _ Great Gray Owl, *Strix nebulosa*

_ _ _ _ Long-eared Owl, *Asio otus*

_ _ _ _ Short-eared Owl, *Asio flammeus*

_ _ _ _ Boreal Owl, *Aegolius funereus*

_ _ _ _ Northern Saw-whet Owl, *Aegolius acadicus*

GOATSUCKERS

_ _ _ _ Lesser Nighthawk, *Chordeiles acutipennis*

_ _ _ _ Common Nighthawk, *Chordeiles minor*

_ _ _ _ Common Poorwill, *Phalaenoptilus nuttallii*

_ _ _ _ Whip-poor-will, *Caprimulgus vociferus*

SWIFTS AND HUMMINGBIRDS

_ _ _ _ Black Swift, *Cypseloides niger*

_ _ _ _ Chimney Swift, *Chaetura pelagica*

_ _ _ _ Vaux's Swift, *Chaetura vauxi*

	♂	♀	Juv.	Imm.
White-throated Swift, *Aeronautes saxatalis*	—	—	—	—
Broad-billed Hummingbird, *Cynanthus latirostris*	—	—	—	—
Blue-throated Hummingbird, *Lampornis clemenciae*	—	—	—	—
Magnificent Hummingbird, *Eugenes fulgens*	—	—	—	—
Lucifer Hummingbird, *Calothorax lucifer*	—	—	—	—
Ruby-throated Hummingbird, *Archilochus colubris*	—	—	—	—
Black-chinned Hummingbird, *Archilochus alexandri*	—	—	—	—
Anna's Hummingbird, *Calypte anna*	—	—	—	—
Costa's Hummingbird, *Calypte costae*	—	—	—	—
Calliope Hummingbird, *Stellula calliope*	—	—	—	—
Broad-tailed Hummingbird, *Selasphorus platycercus*	—	—	—	—
Rufous Hummingbird, *Selasphorus rufus*	—	—	—	—

	♂	♀	Juv.	Imm.
Allen's Hummingbird, *Selasphorus sasin*				

TROGONS, KINGFISHERS, WOODPECKERS, AND ALLIES

	♂	♀	Juv.	Imm.
Elegant Trogon, *Trogon elegans*	—	—	—	—
Belted Kingfisher, *Ceryle alcyon*	—	—	—	—
Green Kingfisher, *Chloroceryle americana*	—	—	—	—
Lewis' Woodpecker, *Melanerpes lewis*	—	—	—	—
Red-headed Woodpecker, *Melanerpes erythrocephalus*	—	—	—	—
Acorn Woodpecker, *Melanerpes formicivorus*	—	—	—	—
Gila Woodpecker, *Melanerpes uropygialis*	—	—	—	—
Yellow-bellied Sapsucker, *Sphyrapicus varius*	—	—	—	—
Red-naped Sapsucker, *Sphyrapicus nuchalis*	—	—	—	—
Red-breasted Sapsucker, *Sphyrapicus ruber*	—	—	—	—
Williamson's Sapsucker, *Sphyrapicus thyroideus*	—	—	—	—

♂ ♀ Juv. Imm.

_ _ _ _ Ladder-backed
Woodpecker,
Picoides scalaris

_ _ _ _ Nuttall's
Woodpecker,
Picoides nuttallii

_ _ _ _ Downy
Woodpecker,
Picoides pubescens

_ _ _ _ Hairy Woodpecker,
Picoides villosus

_ _ _ _ Strickland's
Woodpecker,
*Picoides
stricklandi*

_ _ _ _ White-headed
Woodpecker,
*Picoides
albolarvatus*

_ _ _ _ Three-toed
Woodpecker,
*Picoides
tridactylus*

_ _ _ _ Black-backed
Woodpecker,
Picoides arcticus

_ _ _ _ Northern Flicker,
Colaptes auratus

_ _ _ _ Pileated
Woodpecker,
Dryocopus pileatus

FLYCATCHERS

_ _ _ _ Olive-sided
Flycatcher,
*Mionectes
olivaceus*

_ _ _ _ Greater Pewee,
Contopus pertinax

_ _ _ _ Western Wood-
Pewee, *Contopus
sordidulus*

♂ ♀ Juv. Imm.

_ _ _ _ Eastern Wood-
Pewee, *Contopus
virens*

_ _ _ _ Alder Flycatcher,
*Empidonax
alnorum*

_ _ _ _ Willow Flycatcher,
Empidonax traillii

_ _ _ _ Least Flycatcher,
*Empidonax
minimus*

_ _ _ _ Hammond's
Flycatcher,
*Empidonax
hammondii*

_ _ _ _ Dusky Flycatcher,
*Empidonax
oberholseri*

_ _ _ _ Gray Flycatcher,
*Empidonax
wrightii*

_ _ _ _ Western Flycatcher,
*Empidonax
difficilis*

_ _ _ _ Buff-breasted
Flycatcher,
*Empidonax
fulvifrons*

_ _ _ _ Black Phoebe,
Sayornis nigricans

_ _ _ _ Eastern Phoebe,
Sayornis phoebe

_ _ _ _ Say's Phoebe,
Sayornis saya

_ _ _ _ Vermilion
Flycatcher,
*Pyrocephalus
rubinus*

_ _ _ _ Ash-throated
Flycatcher,
*Myiarchus
cinerascens*

	♂	♀	Juv.	Imm.

Great Crested Flycatcher, *Myiarchus crinitus* — — — —

Brown-crested Flycatcher, *Myiarchus tyrannulus* — — — —

Sulphur-bellied Flycatcher, *Myiodynastes luteiventris* — — — —

Tropical Kingbird, *Tyrannus melancholicus* — — — —

Cassin's Kingbird, *Tyrannus vociferans* — — — —

Western Kingbird, *Tyrannus verticalis* — — — —

Eastern Kingbird, *Tyrannus tyrannus* — — — —

Scissor-tailed Flycatcher, *Tyrannus forficatus* — — — —

Rose-throated Becard, *Pachyramphus aglaiae* — — — —

LARKS AND SWALLOWS

Horned Lark, *Eremophila alpestris* — — — —

Purple Martin, *Progne subis* — — — —

Tree Swallow, *Tachycineta bicolor* — — — —

	♂	♀	Juv.	Imm.

Violet-green Swallow, *Tachycineta thalassina* — — — —

Northern Rough-winged Swallow, *Stelgidopteryx serripennis* — — — —

Bank Swallow, *Riparia riparia* — — — —

Cliff Swallow, *Hirundo pyrrhonota* — — — —

Cave Swallow, *Hirundo fulva* — — — —

Barn Swallow, *Hirundo rustica* — — — —

JAYS, MAGPIES, AND CROWS

Gray Jay, *Perisoreus canadensis* — — — —

Steller's Jay, *Cyanocitta stelleri* — — — —

Scrub Jay, *Aphelocoma coerulescens* — — — —

Gray-breasted Jay, *Aphelocoma ultramarina* — — — —

Pinyon Jay, *Gymnorhinus cyanocephalus* — — — —

Clark's Nutcracker, *Nucifraga columbiana* — — — —

Black-billed Magpie, *Pica pica* — — — —

♂	♀	Juv.	Imm.	
—	—	—	—	Yellow-billed Magpie, *Pica nuttalli*
—	—	—	—	American Crow, *Corvus brachyrhynchos*
—	—	—	—	Northwestern Crow, *Corvus caurinus*
—	—	—	—	Chihuahuan Raven, *Corvus cryptoleucus*
—	—	—	—	Common Raven, *Corvus corax*

CHICKADEES, TITMICE; AND ALLIES

♂	♀	Juv.	Imm.	
—	—	—	—	Black-capped Chickadee, *Parus atricapillus*
—	—	—	—	Mexican Chickadee, *Parus sclateri*
—	—	—	—	Mountain Chickadee, *Parus gambeli*
—	—	—	—	Boreal Chickadee, *Parus hudsonicus*
—	—	—	—	Chestnut-backed Chickadee, *Parus rufescens*
—	—	—	—	Bridled Titmouse, *Parus wollweberi*
—	—	—	—	Plain Titmouse, *Parus inornatus*
—	—	—	—	Tufted Titmouse, *Parus bicolor*
—	—	—	—	Verdin, *Auriparus flaviceps*
—	—	—	—	Bushtit, *Psaltriparus minimus*

NUTHATCHES, CREEPERS, WRENS, AND DIPPERS

♂	♀	Juv.	Imm.	
—	—	—	—	Red-breasted Nuthatch, *Sitta canadensis*
—	—	—	—	White-breasted Nuthatch, *Sitta carolinensis*
—	—	—	—	Pygmy Nuthatch, *Sitta pygmaea*
—	—	—	—	Brown Creeper, *Certhia americana*
—	—	—	—	Cactus Wren, *Campylorhynchus brunneicapilus*
—	—	—	—	Rock Wren, *Salpinctes obsoletus*
—	—	—	—	Canyon Wren, *Catherpes mexicanus*
—	—	—	—	Carolina Wren, *Thryothorus ludovicianus*
—	—	—	—	Bewick's Wren, *Thryomanes bewickii*
—	—	—	—	House Wren, *Troglodytes aedon*
—	—	—	—	Winter Wren, *Troglodytes troglodytes*
—	—	—	—	Sedge Wren, *Cistothorus platensis*
—	—	—	—	Marsh Wren, *Cistothorus palustris*
—	—	—	—	American Dipper, *Cinclus mexicanus*

KINGLETS, GNATCATCHERS, FLYCATCHERS, AND ALLIES

♂ ♀ Juv. Imm.

Golden-crowned Kinglet, *Regulus satrapa* — — — —

Ruby-crowned Kinglet, *Regulus calendula* — — — —

Blue-gray Gnatcatcher, *Polioptila caerulea* — — — —

Black-tailed Gnatcatcher, *Polioptila melanura* — — — —

Northern Wheatear, *Oenanthe oenanthe* — — — —

Eastern Bluebird, *Sialia sialis* — — — —

Western Bluebird, *Sialia mexicana* — — — —

Mountain Bluebird, *Sialia currucoides* — — — —

Townsend's Solitaire, *Myadestes townsendi*

Veery, *Catharus fuscescens* — — — —

Gray-cheeked Thrush, *Catharus minimus* — — — —

Swainson's Thrush, *Catharus ustulatus* — — — —

Hermit Thrush, *Catharus guttatus* — — — —

American Robin, *Turdus migratorius* — — — —

Varied Thrush, *Ixoreus naevius*

♂ ♀ Juv. Imm.

Varied Thrush, *Ixoreus naevius* — — — —

Wrentit, *Chamaea fasciata* — — — —

MOCKINGBIRDS, THRASHERS, AND PIPITS

Gray Catbird, *Dumetella carolinensis* — — — —

Northern Mockingbird, *Mimus polyglottos* — — — —

Sage Thrasher, *Oreoscoptes montanus* — — — —

Brown Thrasher, *Toxostoma rufum* — — — —

Bendire's Thrasher, *Toxostoma bendirei* — — — —

Curve-billed Thrasher, *Toxostoma curvirostre* — — — —

California Thrasher, *Toxostoma redivivum* — — — —

Crissal Thrasher, *Toxostoma dorsale* — — — —

LeConte's Thrasher, *Toxostoma lecontei* — — — —

Water Pipit, *Anthus spinoletta* — — — —

Sprague's Pipit, *Anthus spragueii* — — — —

♂	♀	Juv.	Imm.	WAXWINGS, PHAINOPEPLA, SHRIKES, STARLINGS, AND VIREOS
—	—	—	—	Bohemian Waxwing, *Bombycilla garrulus*
—	—	—	—	Cedar Waxwing, *Bombycilla cedrorum*
—	—	—	—	Phainopepla, *Phainopepla nitens*
—	—	—	—	Northern Shrike, *Lanius excubitor*
—	—	—	—	Loggerhead Shrike, *Lanius ludovicianus*
—	—	—	—	European Starling, *Sturnus vulgaris*
—	—	—	—	Bell's Vireo, *Vireo bellii*
—	—	—	—	Black-capped Vireo, *Vireo atricapillus*
—	—	—	—	Gray Vireo, *Vireo vicinior*
—	—	—	—	Solitary Vireo, *Vireo solitarius*
—	—	—	—	Yellow-throated Vireo, *Vireo flavifrons*
—	—	—	—	Hutton's Vireo, *Vireo huttoni*
—	—	—	—	Warbling Vireo, *Vireo gilvus*
—	—	—	—	Philadelphia Vireo, *Vireo philadelphicus*
—	—	—	—	Red-eyed Vireo, *Vireo olivaceus*

♂	♀	Juv.	Imm.	WARBLERS
—	—	—	—	Tennessee Warbler, *Vermivora peregrina*
—	—	—	—	Orange-crowned Warbler, *Vermivora celata*
—	—	—	—	Nashville Warbler, *Vermivora ruficapilla*
—	—	—	—	Virginia's Warbler, *Vermivora virginiae*
—	—	—	—	Colima Warbler, *Vermivora crissalis*
—	—	—	—	Lucy's Warbler, *Vermivora luciae*
—	—	—	—	Northern Parula, *Parula americana*
—	—	—	—	Tropical Parula, *Parula pitiayumi*
—	—	—	—	Yellow Warbler, *Dendroica petechia*
—	—	—	—	Chestnut-sided Warbler, *Dendroica pensylvanica*
—	—	—	—	Cape May Warbler, *Dendroica tigrina*
—	—	—	—	Black-throated Blue Warbler, *Dendroica caerulescens*
—	—	—	—	Yellow-rumped Warbler, *Dendroica coronata*
—	—	—	—	Black-throated Gray Warbler, *Dendroica nigrescens*
—	—	—	—	Townsend's Warbler, *Dendroica townsendi*

	♂	♀	Juv.	Imm.

Hermit Warbler, *Dendroica occidentalis* — — — —

Black-throated Green Warbler, *Dendroica virens* — — — —

Golden-cheeked Warbler, *Dendroica chrysoparia* — — — —

Blackburnian Warbler, *Dendroica fusca* — — — —

Grace's Warbler, *Dendroica graciae* — — — —

Palm Warbler, *Dendroica palmarum* — — — —

Bay-breasted Warbler, *Dendroica castanea* — — — —

Blackpoll Warbler, *Dendroica striata* — — — —

Black-and-white Warbler, *Mniotilta varia* — — — —

American Redstart, *Setophaga ruticilla* — — — —

Ovenbird, *Seiurus aurocapillus* — — — —

Northern Waterthrush, *Seiurus noveboracensis* — — — —

Connecticut Warbler, *Oporornis agilis* — — — —

Mourning Warbler, *Oporornis philadelphia* — — — —

MacGillivray's Warbler, *Oporornis tolmiei* — — — —

Common Yellowthroat, *Geothlypis trichas* — — — —

Wilson's Warbler, *Wilsonia pusilla* — — — —

Canada Warbler, *Wilsonia canadensis* — — — —

Red-faced Warbler, *Cardellina rubrifrons* — — — —

Painted Redstart, *Myioborus pictus* — — — —

Yellow-breasted Chat, *Icteria virens* — — — —

Olive Warbler, *Peucedramus taeniatus* — — — —

TANAGERS, CARDINALS, AND GROSBEAKS

Hepatic Tanager, *Piranga flava* — — — —

Summer Tanager, *Piranga rubra* — — — —

Scarlet Tanager, *Piranga olivacea* — — — —

Western Tanager, *Piranga ludoviciana* — — — —

Northern Cardinal, *Cardinalis cardinalis* — — — —

Pyrrhuloxia, *Cardinalis sinuatus* — — — —

Rose-breasted Grosbeak, *Pheucticus ludovicianus* — — — —

__ __ __ __ Black-headed Grosbeak, *Pheucticus melanocephalus*

__ __ __ __ Blue Grosbeak, *Guiraca caerulea*

__ __ __ __ Lazuli Bunting, *Passerina amoena*

__ __ __ __ Indigo Bunting, *Passerina cyanea*

__ __ __ __ Varied Bunting, *Passerina versicolor*

__ __ __ __ Painted Bunting, *Passerina ciris*

__ __ __ __ Dickcissel, *Spiza americana*

TOWHEES, SPARROWS, AND ALLIES

__ __ __ __ Green-tailed Towhee, *Pipilo chlorurus*

__ __ __ __ Rufous-sided Towhee, *Pipilo erythrophthalmus*

__ __ __ __ Brown Towhee, *Pipilo fuscus*

__ __ __ __ Abert's Towhee, *Pipilo aberti*

__ __ __ __ Botteri's Sparrow, *Aimophila botterii*

__ __ __ __ Cassin's Sparrow, *Aimophila cassinii*

__ __ __ __ Rufous-winged Sparrow, *Aimophila carpalis*

__ __ __ __ Rufous-crowned Sparrow, *Aimophila ruficeps*

__ __ __ __ American Tree Sparrow, *Spizella arborea*

__ __ __ __ Chipping Sparrow, *Spizella passerina*

__ __ __ __ Clay-colored Sparrow, *Spizella pallida*

__ __ __ __ Brewer's Sparrow, *Spizella breweri*

__ __ __ __ Field Sparrow, *Spizella pusilla*

__ __ __ __ Black-chinned Sparrow, *Spizella atrogularis*

__ __ __ __ Vesper Sparrow, *Pooecetes gramineus*

__ __ __ __ Lark Sparrow, *Chondestes grammacus*

__ __ __ __ Black-throated Sparrow, *Amphispiza bilineata*

__ __ __ __ Sage Sparrow, *Amphispiza belli*

__ __ __ __ Lark Bunting, *Calamospiza melanocorys*

__ __ __ __ Savannah Sparrow, *Passerculus sandwichensis*

__ __ __ __ Baird's Sparrow, *Ammodramus bairdii*

__ __ __ __ Grasshopper Sparrow, *Ammodramus savannarum*

	♂	♀	Juv.	Imm.

Henslow's Sparrow,
*Ammodramus
henslowii* — — — —

LeConte's Sparrow,
*Ammodramus
leconteii* — — — —

Sharp-tailed
Sparrow,
*Ammodramus
caudacutus* — — — —

Fox Sparrow,
Passerella iliaca — — — —

Song Sparrow,
Melospiza melodia — — — —

Lincoln's Sparrow,
Melospiza lincolnii — — — —

Swamp Sparrow,
*Melospiza
georgiana* — — — —

White-throated
Sparrow,
*Zonotrichia
albicollis* — — — —

Golden-crowned
Sparrow,
*Zonotrichia
atricapilla* — — — —

White-crowned
Sparrow,
*Zonotrichia
leucophrys* — — — —

Harris' Sparrow,
*Zonotrichia
querula* — — — —

Dark-eyed Junco,
Junco hyemalis — — — —

Yellow-eyed Junco,
Junco phaeonotus — — — —

McCown's
Longspur,
*Calcarius
mccownii* — — — —

	♂	♀	Juv.	Imm.

Lapland Longspur,
*Calcarius
lapponicus* — — — —

Smith's Longspur,
Calcarius pictus — — — —

Chestnut-collared
Longspur,
Calcarius ornatus — — — —

Snow Bunting,
*Plectrophenax
nivalis* — — — —

MEADOWLARKS, BLACKBIRDS, AND ORIOLES

Bobolink,
*Dolichonyx
oryzivorus* — — — —

Red-winged
Blackbird, *Agelaius
phoeniceus* — — — —

Tricolored
Blackbird, *Agelaius
tricolor* — — — —

Eastern
Meadowlark,
Sturnella magna — — — —

Western
Meadowlark,
Sturnella neglecta — — — —

Yellow-headed
Blackbird,
*Xanthocephalus
xanthocephalus* — — — —

Rusty Blackbird,
*Euphagus
carolinus* — — — —

Brewer's Blackbird,
*Euphagus
cyanocephalus* — — — —

The
Maps

Following are selected geographic range maps for some of the more commonly seen species of the region. Included here are maps showing distribution for breeding, wintering, and resident ranges. No range map can be entirely definitive, and those included here provide *general parameters* of geographic ranges for selected species. The maps indicate the activities of various species only west of the 100th meridian in North America.

Resident species are defined as those that are nonmigratory, regularly residing in a given area. The distribution of the migratory species is described as either "breeding" or "wintering," in that the bird is usually in one or the other locale during the year. However, some migratory birds do have resident ranges, usually in the area between the breeding and wintering ranges. In order to keep these maps concise, some resident ranges for migrants have not been included. In some cases, the species may be in the same locale both when it is breeding and wintering, or the range may overlap.

It is important to remember that a species will be found only in appropriate habitats within its range. Note that our winter is actually summer for visiting seabirds that winter south of the equator.

Colors and patterns are used on these maps to distinguish species and behavior. For the most part, two species are shown on a single map, each species indicated by the use of an individual color. The varying patterns on the maps indicate the different ranges of particular activities, such as breeding, wintering, or resident status, of a bird. A winter range is shown by the use of a lined pattern, whereas a dot pattern indicates the breeding locale of the species. A tone of the species' color shows resident ranges. If a third color appears (purple or orange), it is not an indication of another activity: It means that the regions for the activities shown for the two species are overlapping.

Range and distribution information is often very useful in making a definitive identification, and should be used in conjunction with other identifying techniques whenever possible. Very often a bird can be eliminated as the one having been assumed to have been sighted because it does not conform to the known range or behaviors of the presumed sighted species.

Maps read
left to right;
labels read
top to bottom

 Breeding

||| Wintering

Resident

....

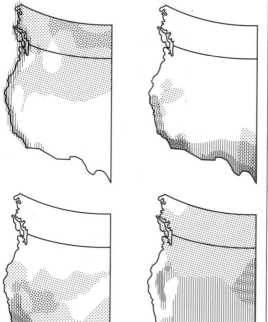

Common
Loon ●

Western
Grebe ●

Least Bittern ●

Great Egret ●

Green backed
Heron ●

White faced
Ibis ●

Snow Goose ●

Canada
Goose ●

Green winged
Teal ●

Cinnamon
Teal ●

Mallard ●

Northern
Pintail ●

Turkey
Vulture ●

Bald Eagle ●

Golden
Eagle ●

Northern
Harrier ●

Sharp-shinned
Hawk ●

Red-tailed
Hawk ●

Prairie
Falcon ●

THE MAPS

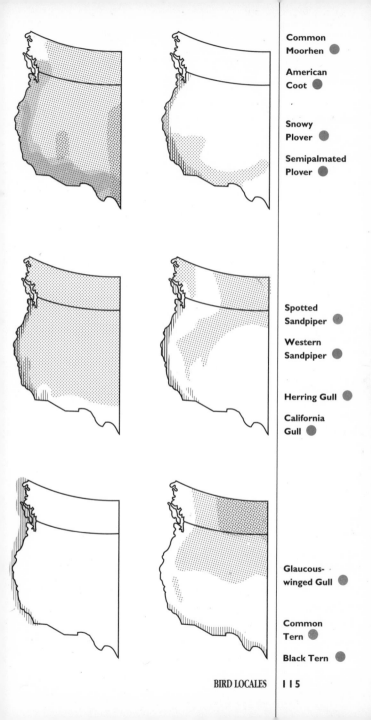

Common
Moorhen

American
Coot

Snowy
Plover

Semipalmated
Plover

Spotted
Sandpiper

Western
Sandpiper

Herring Gull

California
Gull

Glaucous-
winged Gull

Common
Tern

Black Tern

BIRD LOCALES   115

Band-tailed Pigeon ●

Mourning Dove ●

Greater Roadrunner ●

Common Barn-Owl ●

Ferruginous Pygmy-Owl ●

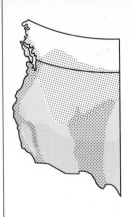

Common Nighthawk ●

Common Poorwill ●

Ann's Hummingbird ●

Belted Kingfisher ●

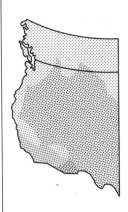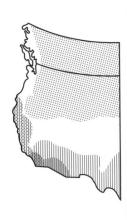

Acorn Woodpecker ●

Gila Woodpecker ●

Hairy Woodpecker ●

Northern Flicker ●

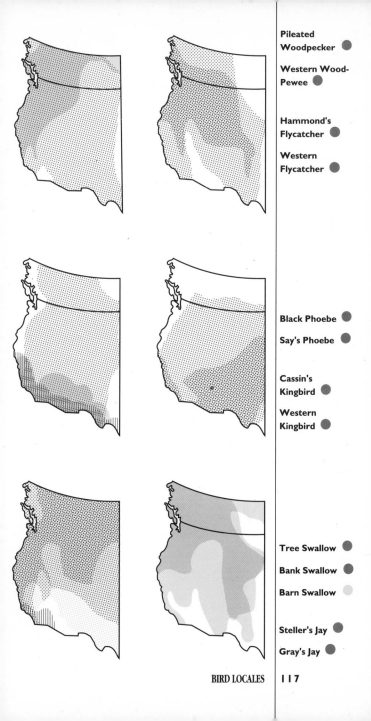

Pileated Woodpecker ●

Western Wood-Pewee ●

Hammond's Flycatcher ●

Western Flycatcher ●

Black Phoebe ●

Say's Phoebe ●

Cassin's Kingbird ●

Western Kingbird ●

Tree Swallow ●

Bank Swallow ●

Barn Swallow ●

Steller's Jay ●

Gray's Jay ●

Scrub Jay ●

American
Crow ●

Mountain
Chickadee ●

Chestnut-
backed
Chickadee ●

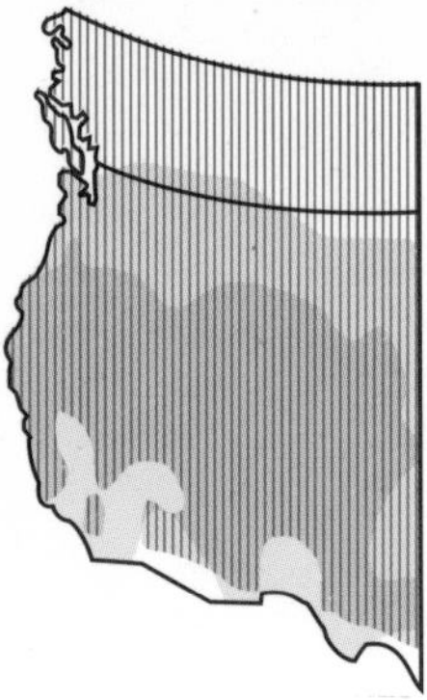

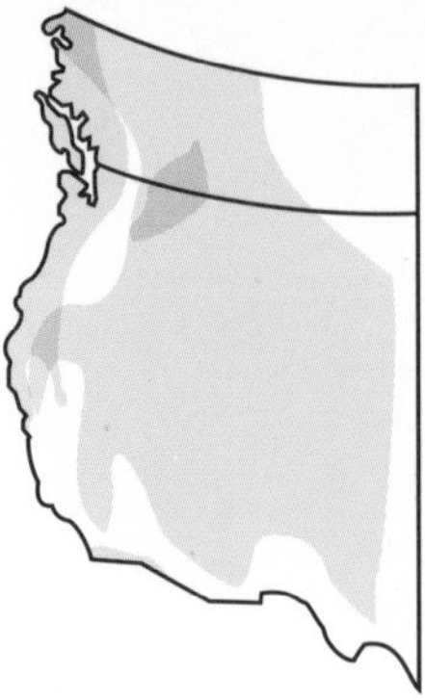

Plain
Titmouse ●

Verdin ●

White-breasted
Nuthatch ●

Brown
Creeper ●

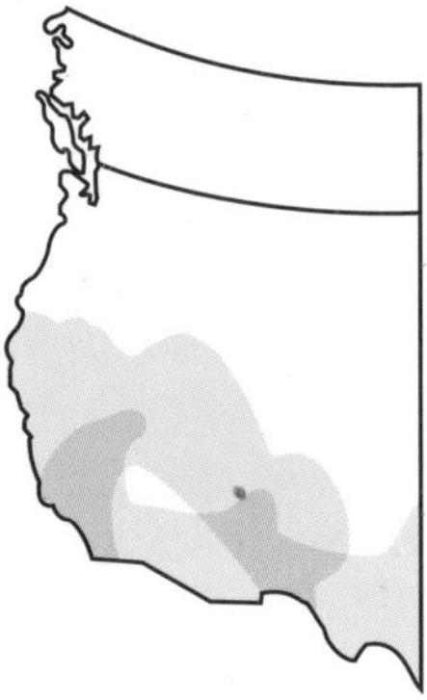

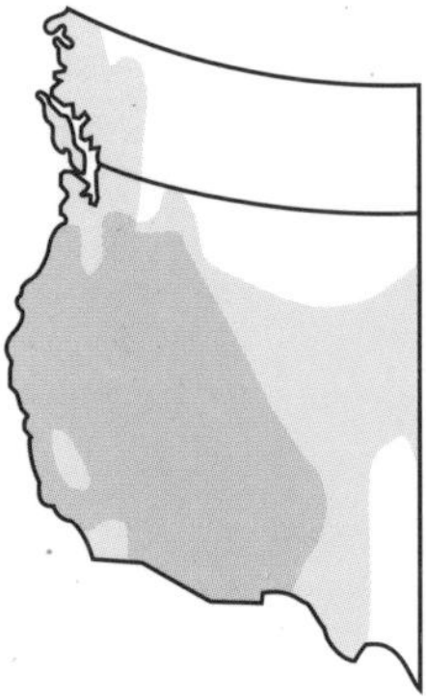

Cactus Wren ●

Bewick's Wren ●

House Wren ●

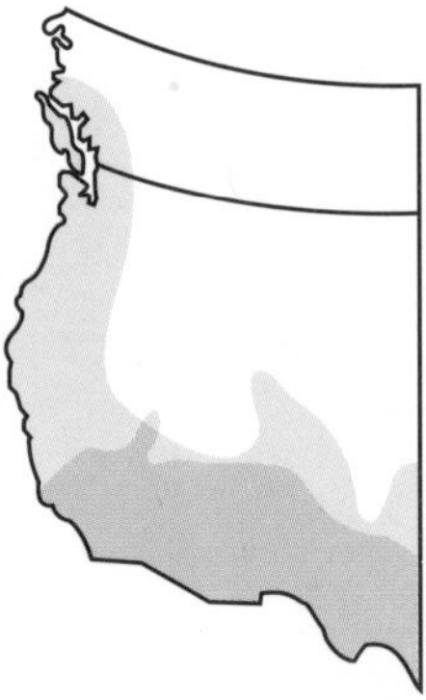

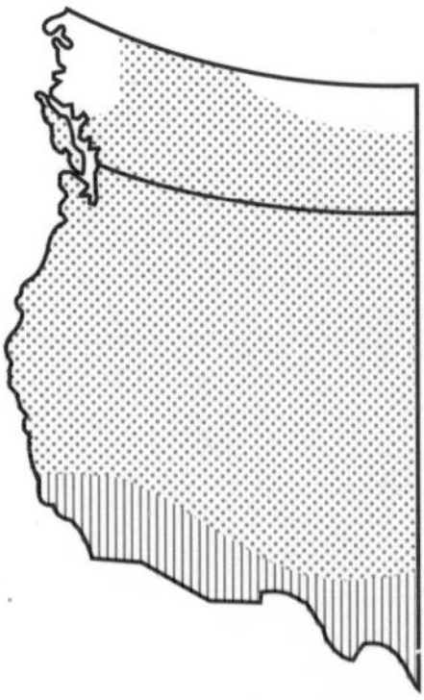

THE MAPS

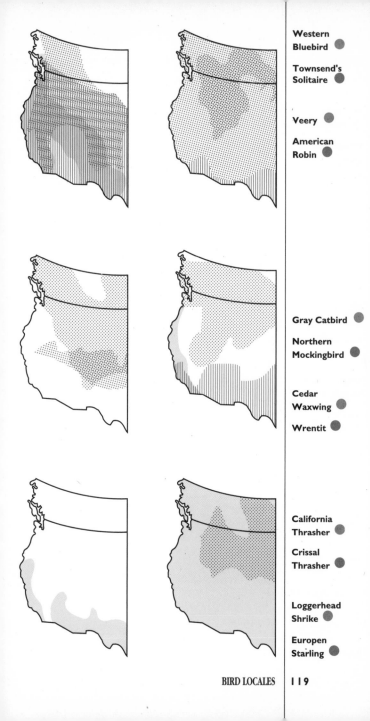

Western Bluebird

Townsend's Solitaire

Veery

American Robin

Gray Catbird

Northern Mockingbird

Cedar Waxwing

Wrentit

California Thrasher

Crissal Thrasher

Loggerhead Shrike

Europen Starling

Hutton's Vireo

Warbling Vireo ●

Orange-crowned Warbler ●

Virginia's Warbler ●

Yellow Warbler ●

Yellow-rumped Warbler ●

Black-throated Gray Warbler ●

Hermit Warbler ●

Grace's Warbler ●

MacGillivray's Warbler ●

Common Yellowthroat ●

Painted Redstart ●

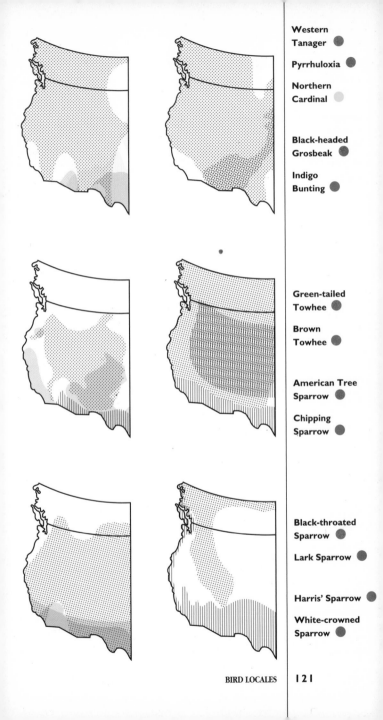

Western Tanager

Pyrrhuloxia

Northern Cardinal

Black-headed Grosbeak

Indigo Bunting

Green-tailed Towhee

Brown Towhee

American Tree Sparrow

Chipping Sparrow

Black-throated Sparrow

Lark Sparrow

Harris' Sparrow

White-crowned Sparrow

Dark-eyed
Junco ●

Tricolored
Blackbird ●

Yellow-headed
Blackbird ●

Brewer's
Blackbird ●

Orchard
Oriole ●

Pine
Grosbeak ●

Purple Finch ●

Pine Siskin ●

House Finch ●

American
Goldfinch ●

Lesser
Goldfinch ●

Competitions

Contact the following organizations for information:

Big Day
American Birding Association
P.O. Box 6599
Colorado Springs, CO 80934
(800) 634-7736

Christmas Bird Count
% C.B.C. Editor
American Birds
National Audubon Society
950 Third Avenue
New York, NY 10022
(212) 832-3200

The World Series of Birding
% Mr. Peter Dunne
Scherman Hoffman
  Sanctuary
New Jersey Audubon Society
P.O. Box 693
Bernardsville, NJ 07924
(908) 766-5787

Audubon, Ornithological, and Naturalist Societies

UNITED STATES

. . . .

N A T I O N A L

American Birding Association
P.O. Box 6599
Colorado Springs, CO 80934
(800) 634-7736

American Ornithologists Union
% National Museum of
  Natural History
Smithsonian Institution
10th and Constitution Avenue
  Northwest
Washington, D.C. 20560
(202) 357-2051

Association of Field Ornithologists
P.O. Box 21618
Columbus, OH 43221

International Council for Bird Preservation
1250 24th Street
  Northeast
Washington, D.C. 20037
(202) 778-9563

National Audubon Society
950 Third Avenue
New York, NY 10022
(212) 832-3200

. . . .

S   T   A   T   E

Contact these societies for local chapters:

Connecticut Audubon Society
2325 Burr Street
Fairfield, CT 06430
(203) 259–6305

Florida Audubon Society
1101 Audubon Way
Maitland, FL 32651
(305) 647–2615

Hawaii Audubon Society
P.O. Box 22832
Honolulu, HI 96822

Illinois Audubon Society
P.O. Box 608
Wayne, IL 60184
(312) 584–6290

Indiana Audubon Society
Mary Gray Bird Sanctuary
RR6
Connersville, IN 47331
(317) 825–9788

Maine Audubon Society
Gilsland Farm
118 Route 1
Falmouth, ME 04105
(207) 781–2330

Massachusetts Audubon Society, Inc.
South Great Road
Lincoln, MA 01773
(617) 259–9500

Michigan Audubon Society
409 West E. Avenue
Kalamazoo, MI 49007
(616) 344–8648

Audubon Society of New Hampshire
3 Silk Farm Road
P.O. Box 528B
Concord, NH 03301
(603) 244–9909

New Jersey Audubon Society
790 Ewing Avenue
P.O. Box 125
Franklin Lake, NJ 07417
(201) 891–1211

Audubon Society of Rhode Island
40 Bowen Street
Providence, RI 02903
(401) 521–1670

C A N A D A

. . . .

N A T I O N A L

Canadian Wildlife Federation
2740 Queensview Drive
Ottawa, Ontario
K2B 1A2
(613) 721-2286

Federation of Ontario Naturalists
355 Lesmill Road
Don Mills, Ontario
M3B 2W8
(416) 444-8419

Federation of B.C. Naturalists
Room 321
1367 West Broadway
Vancouver, B.C.
V6H 4A9
(604) 737-3057

Canadian Nature Federation/Bookshop
453 Sussex Drive
Ottawa, Ontario
KIN 6Z4
(613) 238-6154

Canadian Wildlife Service
351 St. Joseph's Blvd.
17th Floor, P. V. M.
Hull, Quebec
KIA 0H3
(819) 997-1301
(Ontario Head Office)
(819) 953-1412
(Publications Department)

Periodicals

UNITED STATES

Audubon
National Audubon Society
950 Third Avenue
New York, NY 10022
(212) 832-3200
*bimonthly publication free
with membership*

The Auk
American Ornithologists
Union
% National Museum of
Natural History
Smithsonian Institution
10th and Constitution Avenue
Northwest
Washington, D.C. 20560
(202) 357-2051

Birding
American Birding Association
P.O. Box 4335
Austin, TX 78765
(512) 474-4804
bimonthly

The Living Bird Quarterly
Laboratory of Ornithology at
Cornell University
159 Sapsucker Woods Road
Ithaca, NY 14850
(607) 255-7317
free with membership

. . . .

CANADA

*These publications cover all
aspects of wildlife
preservation*

The Canadian Field Naturalist
Ottawa Field Naturalists Club
Box 3264
Postal Station C
Ottawa, ON KIY 4J5
(613) 722-3050

Nature Canada
Canada Nature Federation
75 Albert Street
Ottawa, ON K1P 6G1
(613) 238-6154

Seasons
Federation of Ontario
Naturalists
355 Lesmill Road
Don Mills, ON M3B 2W8
(416) 444-8419

Books

*The A.O.U. Check-list of
North American Birds,* 6th
ed. Lawrence, Kans.: Allen
Press Inc., 1983.

Farrand, John, ed. *The
Audubon Society Master
Guide to Birding.* 3 vols.
New York: Knopf, 1984.

*National Geographic
Society's Field Guide to the
Birds of North America.*
Washington, D.C.: National
Geographic Society, 1983.

Peterson, Roger Tory. *A Field
Guide to the Birds East of
the Rockies,* 4th ed. Boston:
Houghton Mifflin Co., 1980.

———. *A Field Guide to
Western Birds,* 2d ed.
Boston: Houghton Mifflin Co.,
1961.

Robbins, Chandler S., et al.
Birds of North America, rev.
ed. Racine, Wis.: Western
Publishers, 1983.